The Sources of Science
Number 29

THE SOURCES OF SCIENCE

Editor-in-Chief: HARRY WOOLF

WILLIS K. SHEPARD PROFESSOR OF THE HISTORY OF SCIENCE
THE JOHNS HOPKINS UNIVERSITY

1. WALLER: Essayes of Natural Experiments

   WITH A NEW INTRODUCTION BY A. RUPERT HALL

2. BOYLE: Experiments and Considerations Touching Colours

   WITH A NEW INTRODUCTION BY MARIE BOAS HALL

3. NEWTON: The Mathematical Works of Isaac Newton, 2 vols.

   WITH A NEW INTRODUCTION BY DEREK T. WHITESIDE

4. LIEBIG: Animal Chemistry

   WITH A NEW INTRODUCTION BY FREDERIC L. HOLMES

5. KEPLER: Kepler's Conversation with Galileo's Sidereal Messenger

   TRANSLATED AND EDITED BY EDWARD ROSEN

6. FARADAY: Achievements of Michael Faraday

   WITH A NEW INTRODUCTION BY L. PEARCE WILLIAMS

7. TAYLOR: Scientific Memoirs Selected from the Transactions of Foreign Academies of Science and Learned Societies, and from Foreign Journals, 7 vols.

   WITH A NEW PREFACE BY HARRY WOOLF

8. CHINCHILLA: Anales Históricas de la Medicina en General y Biográfico-Bibliográficos de la Española en Particular, 4 vols.

WITH A NEW INTRODUCTION BY FRANCISCO GUERRA

9. MOREJÓN: Historia Bibliográfica de la Medicina Española, 7 vols.

WITH A NEW INTRODUCTION BY FRANCISCO GUERRA

10. BULLETTINO DI BIBLIOGRAFIA E DI STORIA DELLE SCIENZE MATEMATICHE E FISICHE, 20 vols.

EDITED BY B. BONCOMPAGNI

11. GREW: The Anatomy of Plants

WITH A NEW INTRODUCTION BY CONWAY ZIRKLE

12. HALLIWELL: A Collection of Letters Illustrative of the Progress of Science in England from the Reign of Queen Elizabeth to That of Charles II

WITH A NEW INTRODUCTION BY CARL B. BOYER

13. THE WORKS OF WILLIAM HARVEY, M.D.

TRANSLATED FROM THE LATIN WITH A LIFE OF THE AUTHOR BY ROBERT WILLIS, M.D.

14. BREWSTER: Memoirs of the Life, Writings, and Discoveries of Sir Isaac Newton

WITH A NEW INTRODUCTION BY RICHARD S. WESTFALL

22. CATALOGUS BIBLIOTHECAE HISTORICO-NATURALIS JOSEPHI BANKS, 5 vols.

COMPILED BY JONAS DRYANDER

23. DELAMBRE: Histoire de l'Astronomie Ancienne, 2 vols.

WITH A NEW PREFACE BY OTTO NEUGEBAUER

24. DELAMBRE: Histoire de l'Astronomie du Moyen Age

25. DELAMBRE: Histoire de l'Astronomie Moderne

WITH A NEW INTRODUCTION BY I. BERNARD COHEN

26. DARMSTAEDTER: Naturforscher und Erfinder. Biographische Miniaturen

29. MAUPERTUIS: The Earthly Venus

TRANSLATED BY SIMONE BRANGIER BOAS WITH NOTES AND AN INTRODUCTION BY GEORGE BOAS

The Earthly Venus

The Earthly Venus

by

Pierre-Louis Moreau

de MAUPERTUIS

Translated from

VENUS PHYSIQUE

(*Les Oeuvres de Maupertuis*, T.2, Berlin and Lyon, 1753)

by

SIMONE BRANGIER BOAS

With Notes and an Introduction
by
GEORGE BOAS
PROFESSOR EMERITUS OF THE HISTORY OF PHILOSOPHY
THE JOHNS HOPKINS UNIVERSITY
BALTIMORE, MARYLAND

The Sources of Science, No. 29

Johnson Reprint Corporation
New York and London

1966

Prefatory Note

All footnotes in the original edition of "Vénus Physique" have been printed as given by Maupertuis. But since he usually did not identify the authors or even the articles to which he was referring, the addenda have been supplied by the annotator. These, together with the translation of the Latin quotations and French titles, are enclosed in square brackets. Any note followed by the initial "A." has been written by the annotator.

The translator has tried to be faithful to the literary style of Maupertuis and has kept his terminology as far as seemed clear even when it is in conflict with present usage. Thus she has used the words *Philosopher* and *Physicist* when they occur in the text, though usually Maupertuis means simply *scientist*. To do otherwise would have been anachronistic and, since the translation has been made in the interest of history, she has felt that anachronisms should be avoided when possible.

S.B.B.

G.B.

Contents

Prefatory Note ix

Introduction xiii

PART I: *Concerning the Origin of Animals*

Chapter 1. Introduction 3

Chapter 2. Theories of Generation among
the Ancients 7

Chapter 3. The Theory of Ovism 9

Chapter 4. Doctrine of Spermatic Animals . . 14

Chapter 5. Intermediate System 19

Chapter 6. Observations for and against Eggs . 20

Chapter 7. Harvey's Experiments 23

Chapter 8. Harvey's Views of Generation . . 28

Chapter 9. Attempts to Reconcile Observations
with Ovism 29

Chapter 10. Attempts to Reconcile These
Observations with the Theory of
Spermatic Animalcules 30

Chapter 11. Variety among Animals . . . 32

Chapter 12. Thoughts on Systems of Growth . . 40

Chapter 13. Reasons Which Prove That Both the
Father and the Mother Participate in
the Embryo's Production 43

Chapter 14. Theories Concerning Monsters . . 45

Chapter 15. Accidents Brought on by the
Imagination of Mothers 48

Chapter 16. Difficulties Encountered in Ovism and
the Theory of Spermatic Animalcules . 51
Chapter 17. Hypotheses on the Formation of the
Fetus 54
Chapter 18. Hypotheses on the Function of
Spermatic Animalcules 59
PART II: *Varieties in the Species of Man*
Chapter 1. Distribution of the Different Races of
Man, According to the Earth's
Different Areas 63
Chapter 2. An Explanation of the Phenomenon of
Color Difference in Ovism and
Animalculism 69
Chapter 3. Production of New Species . . . 71
Chapter 4. White Negroes 75
Chapter 5. Attempt at an Explanation of the
Preceding Phenomena 78
Chapter 6. That It Is Rarer to Have Black Children
Born of White Parents, Than White
Children of Black Parents. That the
Original Parents of the Human Race
Were White. The Difficulty of the
Origin of the Black Is Raised . . 81
Chapter 7. Why Should the Blacks Be Found Only
in the Torrid Zone and Dwarfs and
Giants Near the Poles? . . . 84
CONCLUSION. *Doubts and Questions* . . . 85

Introduction

I

Pierre-Louis Moreau de Maupertuis was born in Saint-Malo on September 28, 1698. A sickly child, spoiled by his mother, he came to admit his inability to stand opposition and indeed his later career showed how oversensitive he was to criticism, though modest in his claims. He began his education at home under the direction of the Abbé Coquaud and subsequently went to Paris where he entered the Collège de la Marche and remained for two years. Finding this unsatisfactory, he returned home and after a year or two of travel and desultory searching for a vocation, he began the study of mathematics, which eventually took him to Basel. Here he studied with Jean Bernoulli and formed a friendship with this family of mathematicians that lasted throughout his life.

Meanwhile he had entered the army and completed a term of two years in the musketeers, rising to the rank of captain of cavalry. Military service in those days was not so absorbing as it has become in our own era, and Maupertuis was able to continue his mathematical studies as well as to frequent the society of intellectuals who met for dinner and conversation at the famous Café Procope, a group which included Nicole, Marivaux, Terrason, and Fréret, all of whom rose to eminence in the eighteenth century. Nicole, who had worked in the field of probability, seems to have had a special influence upon the young savant, and it was at his suggestion that Mauper-

tuis began writing treatises on mathematical subjects. But
Maupertuis also became interested in biological problems
and from then on explored the two fields contemporane-
ously. Thus in one year he submitted to the Académie des
Sciences a paper on "Observations and experiments on a
species of salamander" as well as one "On the quadrature
and rectification of figures formed by rolling regular poly-
gons." The former, which is of more interest here than
the latter, showed that where natural science was concerned, Maupertuis believed strongly in the experimental
method, a belief that appears throughout the "Earthly
Venus." Though he was more interested in refuting certain superstitions that had been regnant since antiquity,
such as the incombustibility of these little creatures, at the
same time he found evidence of something that was, he
thought, of primary importance to theories of generation.
At the end of this essay he says, "When I had opened up
some salamanders, I was surprised to find at the same
time both eggs and even little ones as perfect as those of
viviparous animals. The eggs formed two clusters similar to the ovaries of birds, except that they were more
elongated. And the little ones were enclosed in two long
tubes, the tissues of which were so thin that one could
see through them very distinctly. I counted in one salamander forty-two young and in another fifty-four, almost
all alive, as well-formed as adult salamanders and more
agile. These animals, "he continues," appear fully suited to
clear up the mystery of generation, for, no matter how
great the variety of nature, the heart of things is always
about the same. We all know what advantages are to be
derived from comparative anatomy; the perfect knowledge
of a single body is perhaps no more than the price one

pays for the impossible examination of all the bodies in nature."[1]

In 1728 Maupertuis went to London, where he stayed six months. Pierre Brunet, in his authoritative biography of Maupertuis, quotes a passage from Voltaire's "Lettres anglaises" in which he says, "A Frenchman who arrives in London finds things very different in science [*philosophie*] as in everything else. He left the universe a plenum; he finds it empty. In Paris the universe is seen to be composed of vortices made of subtle matter; in London there is nothing of the sort to be seen. At home it is the moon's pressure which causes the tides; in England it is the sea which gravitates towards the moon. . . . Among your Cartesians everything comes about through an impulsion which is but slightly understood; in the land of Newton all is due to an attraction whose cause is no better known. In Paris you imagine the earth to be made in form of a melon; in London it is flattened at the two poles. Light for a Cartesian exists in the air; for a Newtonian it comes from the sun in six and a half minutes. . . . These are serious conflicts."[2] Serious they obviously are, and to an eager young scientist the problem was to make a choice between them. Maupertuis opted for Newton.

He thus became the first Newtonian in France, a position that earned him the affectionate admiration of Voltaire, endeared him to Mme du Chatelet, and confirmed his reputation as a mathematician. The shape of the earth was of special importance not only to geographers but also

[1] Quoted in Pierre Brunet, "Maupertuis, l'Oeuvre et sa place dans la Pensée Scientifique du XVIIIe siècle," Vol. I, p. 290. Paris, 1929.
[2] *Ibid.*, p. 13.

to mariners. For the determination of longitude was essential to navigation, and if the earth were elongated from north to south or flattened at the poles, clearly one's position at sea would be reckoned differently. The Academy of Science, to which Maupertuis had been elected in 1723, decided to put the two theories to the test. To this end they sent a group of scientists to Peru in 1735 and another as far north as was feasible. The problem was to measure an arc of the meridian at each place. Equipped at the expense of the state with the necessary instruments and given the direction of the northern party, Maupertuis and his companions spent a year in the north of Lapland, undergoing, as may well be imagined, a series of hardships brought on by the lack of civilized conveniences, sparse food supplies, and the climate. The leader of the expedition seems to have been well suited to his task, for he not only reached the scientific goal towards which he was striving, but also kept his staff in good spirits, endured the same hardships they had to undergo, and never asked one of them to face dangers that he would not face himself. There are many testimonies to his great courage and enterprise, and to the meticulous workmanship that he manifested by repeating his measurements. To establish the requisite base-lines in a country covered with thick forests and traversed by swollen rivers was obviously no easy task, especially in winter near the Arctic Circle. The results of the expedition confirmed the inferences that had been made theoretically.

Unfortunately, a conclusion that goes contrary to popular opinion will always be received with suspicion, and in this case national pride was also involved. Maupertuis found to his chagrin that two parties arose in Paris, one supporting and the other opposing him. As he says in one of his letters,[3] "We found on our arrival strong conflicts of opinion. Paris, the inhabitants òf which are incapable of remaining indifferent in any matter, broke into two parties. One group was our partisans; on the other side were those who believed that is was a question of national honor not to give the earth a shape which came from a foreign land, a shape that had been conceived by an Englishman [Newton] and a Dutchman [Huyghens]. They tried to cast doubts on our measurements and indeed we may have upheld them with too much heat. We in turn attacked the measurements that had been made in France. The dispute waxed hotter and soon gave birth to injustice and enmity." But since the measurements taken in Peru confirmed those taken in Lapland, as had been predicted, it had to be granted that Maupertuis was right. Unfortunately the disputes embittered him and may well have been the primary cause of his decision to accept an invitation from Frederick the Great, which was given him in 1740, to go to Berlin to reorganize the Berlin Academy of Sciences. The invitation was probably suggested to the King by Voltaire.

Once in Germany Maupertuis set to work with all the vigor that was characteristic of him. His situation was not an easy one. To begin with, he was a foreigner in Germany, and in France he was criticized as a turncoat. Nevertheless his life was not all bitterness. He met his future wife there, Eleanor von Borck, a maid of honor to the Queen. He also succeeded in inducing several of the most eminent men of science to come there, men such as

[3] Lettre XXI, *in* "Les Oeuvres de M. de Maupertuis," Vol. II, p. 468. Berlin and Lyon, 1753.

Euler, Béguelin, Mérian, and Meckel. By 1746 he had been named president of the Academy and had become one of the most famous scientists in Europe. His letters show a certain contentment in his lot, but trouble soon arose, trouble that aroused the hostility of the man who had called himself his most fervent disciple, Voltaire. If there is any one man responsible for the almost total eclipse of Maupertuis, it is Voltaire. Widely known and respected in his own day, in spite of those critiques that inevitably arise, in the words of Professor Bentley Glass, Maupertuis became "a forgotten scientist, for whose name one must hunt assiduously to find more than a mention in the histories of scientific thought and achievements."[4] The sarcasm of Voltaire was as acid as his admiration had been fulsome. The man who had written to Maupertuis, "Be my master forever in physics and my disciple in friendship; for I mean to love you deeply if you will love me only a bit,"[4a] soon began to ridicule his former "master" as a knave and a fool.

The cause of this rupture was ostensibly Maupertuis's Principle of Least Action. A Swiss mathematician, Samuel Koenig, wrote to his former teacher, Maupertuis, maintaining both that the Principle was erroneous and also that it had been previously discovered by the philosopher Leibniz. The proof of the latter claim—the former was irrelevant—lay in a letter supposed to have been written by the philosopher to one Captain Henzi, who had been beheaded two years before the incident in Berne because

---

[4] Bentley Glass, "Maupertuis, Pioneer of Genetics and Evolution," *in* "Forerunners of Darwin, 1745–1859" (Bentley Glass, Owsei Temkin, and William L. Straus, Jr., eds.), p. 54. Baltimore, 1959.

[4a] See Brunet, *op. cit.,* Vol. I, p. 25.

of his share in a conspiracy against the state. Naturally the Academy demanded a copy of the letter, if the original could not be found. The papers of Henzi had been burned, but in some unexplained fashion Koenig had copies of extracts from it. Yet he was unable or unwilling to produce them. The letter in question was said to have been sent to a man named Hermann who was dead. King Frederick then took the matter in hand and asked the Burgermaster of Basel to have Hermann's papers searched, hoping thus to come upon the original, if it was still extant. But the search was fruitless. Further searches, initiated by the Academy, were equally vain, and finally that body appointed Euler to investigate the whole affair and report upon it. The net result was the decision that since the first fragment sent by Koenig was suspect and the original letter not found, and that furthermore Koenig was unable to indicate where it might be found, "it is plain that his [Koenig's] cause was of the worst and that the fragment was forged either to harm M. de Maupertuis or to increase, as by a pious fraud, the praises of the great Leibniz, who beyond doubt has no need of such help."[5] As soon as Koenig learned of this, he resigned from the Academy, wrote an appeal to the public in self-defense, and stirred up the famous quarrel in which Voltaire supported Koenig while Euler supported Maupertuis.

One might imagine that a man whose mathematical theses were defended by an eminent mathematician might win out in a dispute with a man whose criticism of the same thesis is supported only by a poet, satirist, and playwright. But to imagine this would be to underestimate

[5] Translated from the French as cited by Brunet, *op. cit.*, Vol. I, p. 141.

both the unscrupulousness of Voltaire and his power over public opinion. He had no need to argue about the Principle of Least Action, the moral character of Maupertuis, the history of mathematics, or even the dubiousness of Koenig's story. It is of course possible that Koenig had been taken in by a third party, though who it could have been or why he should have done it is unknown. All Voltaire had to do was to put the issue on the basis of free speech and to lampoon the character of Koenig's adversary in any way he found pleasing. His "Diatribe of Dr. Akakia," his "Micromegas," his sly references in epigrams to the erotic life of his opponent, his insistence on the triviality of determining the exact shape of the earth, all such jibes were calculated to make the salons giggle if not more. But at the same time, why should the man who had learned all that he knew about Newtonian physics turn in so bloodthirsty a manner against his teacher? There must have been more to his change of heart than simple conviction of the truth of Koenig's claims, for if he were interested solely in defending a man's right of free speech, that right belonged as much to Euler and Maupertuis as to Koenig. Unfortunately we have no evidence other than Voltaire's complaints in letters to his niece, and these reveal more of a streak of paranoia than signs of real persecution. But Voltaire made the most of his literary gifts.

Whatever the cause of Maupertuis's loss of fame, the fact remains that he lost it. After serving as president of the Academy of Sciences at Berlin for fourteen years (1742–1756), he received permission from the King to visit his family and home in Saint-Malo. His health was poor, as it always had been, except in Lapland, and he undertook a voyage to Switzerland to see if the mountain air would help him. He grew steadily weaker during the trip and kept interrupting it for rest along the way, at which stops he was received with the greatest kindness by his friends. He finally reached Basel in October, 1758, staying with his lifelong friend, Jean Bernoulli. He tried to continue but his strength gave out and by July, 1759, he was dead.

When one thinks over the contribution of this man to science, one concludes that he was of that number of scientists who are more capable of formulating brilliant ideas than of testing them in a laboratory. It is true that his voyage to Lapland, his dissections of salamanders and scorpions, his attempts to set up statistical tables illustrating heredity, were all instances of a desire to put theory to the test of fact. But it is seldom that a man can be both a practicing scientist and the director of scientific research. We have no way of knowing what he would have achieved if he had been free of the presidency of the Berlin Academy, for the correspondence involved in such a post is alone very time-consuming. One has the feeling, when reading his works, that he was always on the edge of an important discovery but never went beyond that edge. We shall try to make this clearer in what follows.

II

The "Earthly Venus" was written at a time when the theory of preformationism was dominant. This theory maintained that the adult animal was already formed in either what was erroneously believed to be the egg (ovism) or in the spermatozoon (animalculism). The opening chapters of the book undertake a critique of both these theories. Oddly enough, both seemed to hold that only one parent was responsible for the fetus. It was folded up like a flower in its bud, all complete but in miniature form. The spermatozoon was a homunculus and the egg was the container of a similar creature. The growth of the embryo was simply the exfoliation of organs already present in microscopic form.

The mammalian egg was not discovered until 1827, and what the seventeenth- and eighteenth-century scientists took for an egg was really the Graafian follicles, in which are encased the corpora lutea and which do not appear until after an ovum has been discharged. At the time of their discovery by Regnier de Graaf in 1672, the existence of a mammalian egg was no more than a surmise based on analogy with oviparous animals. The drive among scientists was to discover, if possible, general laws which would bridge the apparent gaps between the various groups of living beings. If plants grow from seeds, and reptiles and birds from eggs, why should there not be something similar from which a man or woman might be born? Though the Graafian follicles were not eggs, they seemed to be eggs and the only question that remained was how they developed. It was obvious that they would not develop without previous copulation, but just what that had to do with the question was of course unknown.

Spermatozoa were first found by van Leeuwenhoek's assistant, L. D. Hamm, in 1677, five years after the discovery of the Graafian follicles. Called *spermatic animalcules,* they were clearly living beings, looking, as Maupertuis says, like tadpoles. This being so, one had something already alive which under appropriate circumstances could evolve into a full-grown animal. Where the ovist claimed that the egg contained the animal folded together as a flower is folded within a bud, the animalculist claimed that the animal was present in the spermatozoon. To the former the "male seminal fluid" simply activated the unfolding and growing of the embryo in the egg; to the latter the egg was simply the temporary abiding place of the animalcule, furnishing it with food, shelter, and warmth. Maupertuis took it upon himself to prove that both theories were wrong.

He raised the very simple question of why, if the fetus were merely the exfoliation of a seed that came either from the mother or from the father, children should sometimes inherit their mother's traits and sometimes their father's. For they ought to inherit only those of one parent. It was one of those obvious questions that few people ask. There had been a tradition dating from Aristotle that the contribution of the mother to the child's makeup was food—matter—whereas the father contributed the essential character—form. It may well have been this tradition that influenced scientists to look to one or the other parent for inherited traits, but not to both. Maupertuis, as a matter of fact, went back consciously to Aristotle to prove that each parent contributed something, but he did not accept the theory that matter was contributed by one and form by the other.

He also asked a second question: If either of the regnant theories were true, the children of Negroes and whites should not be mulattoes but either white or black. According to the ovists, the children should be the color of their mother; according to the animalculists, that of their father. To his way of thinking, the fact that they were brown, rather than black or white, was evidence that they inherited their color from both parents. Added to this was substantiation from his study of the genetics of polydactyly. He had data both from his own notes and from those of the famous entomologist, Réaumur, to show that this abnormality ran in families and that it could be handed down from either the mother's or the father's branch of the family tree. Indeed in one case it seemed to have been inherited from a grandparent. In his own notes was a family chart of a family in Berlin, the Ruhes, showing the distribution of polydactyly in four generations. In the first the grandmother had six digits, but the condition of the grandfather was not known. In the second generation, the mother had six digits but the father was normal. This couple apparently had eight children, of whom four were polydactyl. One of these, male, inherited his mother's extra digit, and of his six children by a normal woman, two, both males, were polydactyl and four were normal. The sex of the four normal children is unrecorded. But regardless of the gaps in the record, it was clear that polydactyly could be inherited from either sex and could appear in either sex, regardless of the sex of the polydactyl progenitor.

The second set of data, from Réaumur, was collected from a Maltese couple named Kelleia. This couple was normal as far as their fingers and toes were concerned, though here too the record is incomplete. From this couple a polydactyl son was born who married a normal woman. They had four children, two polydactyl boys, one normal boy, and a polydactyl girl. The normal boy married a normal girl and had several normal children. But of the three others who married, twelve children were born, of whom five were normal and the others, of both sexes, polydactyl.[6] The conclusion of Maupertuis, that characteristics could be inherited from either parent or both, was pretty well confirmed.

This is, to be sure, a commonplace today, but so is the theory of relativity. At the time it was radical, for it destroyed at one blow two theories that had held the field for many years and had been advocated by eminent men of science. But there was more to the matter than that. The recording of genealogical data would have made no sense to either convinced ovists or convinced animalculists. But it later became a practice which anticipated the investigations of men such as Mendel. By its means biologists were able to discover sex-linked characters and mutations, and to distinguish between dominant and recessive traits. Unfortunately human families are harder to trace than those of peas, primroses, and fruit flies. Their progeny are less numerous and appear less rapidly, so that statistical data that might prove significant are rarer. Yet the method was indubitably productive and, as the nineteenth century was to show, the source of one of the great laws of genetics. It may be of interest to recall that Mendel's discoveries too were almost unknown until thirty-five years after their publication.

Having disproved the truth of either dominant theory, Maupertuis now had to set up one of his own. Laboratory equipment in the mid-eighteenth century was not adequate to the problem. But Maupertuis, relying on reasoning, did construct a theory that again anticipated the method of his nineteenth-century successors. That was to think of the

---

[6] See the genealogical charts in Glass *et al., op. cit.,* pp. 65ff.

characteristics of an animal as a collection of individual traits. These unitary characters could be inherited singly or in small clusters without affecting the inheritance of all. We are accustomed to this idea in, for instance, *Drosophila melanogaster,* where eye color, length of wing, and so on, are the traits in question. Maupertuis had to deal with more obvious characteristics, such as arms, legs, shape of nose, hair, and so on. His point was that the "seminal fluids" of both parents were composed of chemical particles which would determine these characters. He knew nothing of chromosomes and genes, nor did anyone else, but he had noted in his own observations and in the records of other scientists, the phenomena under consideration and he had proved that the sex of the parents was irrelevant to how they were passed on to their children. Sex-linked traits, as we have said, he could not establish because of lack of data, though his two human genealogies, if they had been more extensive and if they had indicated the presence or absence of traits other than polydactyly, might have led to that concept, too. The question now remained, what determined which unitary characters would be passed on?

His answer again was a curious half-anticipation of a theory of our own times. For to his way of thinking the problem could be solved only by what we should be likely to call biochemistry. He looked for some chemical principle that would do the work. He found it in the notion of chemical affinity. The particles from which the various organs were to be generated were attracted to others according to definite chemical rules. He found in the formation of crystals a hint of how this might be possible, and used the formation of arborescent silver (the *Arbor*

Dianae) as his principal example,[7] though he says that there are many others that would do as well. Chemical affinity, he believed, is the same force as that which attracts the planets towards the sun, for he never forgot the lessons of Newton. In each of the seminal fluids, to use his own term, there are particles that are destined to form the heart, entrails, arms, and legs, as well as the other organs, and each has a greater affinity for its analogues than for any other particles. Thus the arm-particles from both mother and father unite, and so with the others. And though both sexes produce more seminal fluid than is strictly necessary, when the appropriate unions have been made, the superfluous particles have nothing with which to unite and are wasted. But there are occasions on which the appropriate particles do not unite, and there is born a defective child; there are others on which three particles unite instead of two, and a child with extra organs is born. These he calls *monstres par défaut* and *monstres par excès,* respectively. One of the additional proofs of his thesis is worth recording. When there is an excess of organs, they always occur in the proper place; a child born with two heads does not have one on the lower end of his spine and the other at the upper, or fingers that sprout out of a head or ears out of feet. The union of the seminal particles must therefore follow rules as fixed as the rules describing the movements of the solar system. It is curious to find that the most recent theories of genetics have also discovered that the chromosomes, which are strings of chemicals, are twisted about each other to form a helix, and that here too the genes are arranged in

[7] See translation below, p. 54.

juxtaposition. The principal difference in the logical structures of the modern and the Maupertuian theories is that in the former the laws of chance play a greater role. But after all, if the nucleic acids are the genetic materials, and current opinion says they are, then their behavior will follow whatever laws describe the interactions of chemicals.

The problem now became that of the origin of species. That species had an origin was in itself a moot point as late as the 1840's. For it took another century before the leading scientists were convinced that they had not been created by God just as they are today. As for the general public, it is still against the law in Tennessee to "teach" the theory of organic evolution. Maupertuis approaches this problem not through an inventory of the varieties of lower animals and plants, but directly through those of human beings. He retains his idea of unitary characters, and points to differences in color, height, and hair, or in facial features, and is even willing to consider the possibility that "the inhabitants of the forests of Borneo," presumably the orangutans, are a kind of man. He then points out that the most extraordinary generalization that can be made about the races of man concerns their color, for all the people of the earth who inhabit the tropics are either black or very dark brown. As one moves away from the Equator towards the poles, skin color becomes lighter. In the second place he says that by selective breeding one could produce new varieties of animals and that the same seems to have been done on a smaller scale among human beings. As examples of how certain desired traits are preserved, he uses the cases of the very tall soldiers of the King of Prussia and the tiny-footed women of China. He thought presumably that in time such traits would be perpetuated. In the third place, he brings up the albino Negroes, some of whom are reported to form special social groups, as in Senegal and on the Isthmus of Panama, of both of which he knew only by hearsay. All these traits, he says, could be fixed by heredity, though sometimes they occur as what we should call today mutation. But he also grants that if no deliberate and planned selection is made by an interested party, the more unusual traits will tend to disappear. He is thus confronted with the following situation. On the one hand certain characters can be perpetuated by selective breeding and on the other they will not necessarily remain fixed, if selection is not continued.

To explain this he proposes three hypotheses which, he emphasizes, are only conjectures.

(1) The seminal fluid of every species contains innumerable particles suitable to perpetuate the species.

(2) The seminal fluid of each individual, as contrasted with the species, contains more particles fitted to carry on the traits of the individuals than of others.

(3) Each particle produces what he calls *germs,* which will induce the development of a specific organ. He admits that this is the most hazardous of his three hypotheses and suggests an experiment which was actually tried later by Weismann, to cut off a given organ from a certain type of animal, to repeat this generation after generation, and see whether or not the organ would not tend to disappear. Weismann, as is well known, cut off the tails of several generations of rats, but no tailless rats were born. Whether this would have satisfied Maupertuis, we have no way of knowing. The question of the inheritance of

acquired characters is still debated, in one form or another, though not always by authoritative biologists. In fact, Bernard Shaw, who was hardly a fool, suggested that the experiment should have been tried on some organ of which the animal stood in greater need. But after all who knows what is the need that a rat finds for a tail?

By means of these three hypotheses Maupertuis thought that he was able to explain why children resemble either one or the other of their parents; why sometimes they revert in their characteristics to a grandparent, or an even more remote ancestor; and why certain characters, which are unusual (sports), tend to disappear. He added another factor to his theory, however, which apparently he did not think counted as hypothetical: the influence of the environment.

Climate and food, he maintained, might be favorable or unfavorable to the development of a fetus. And the traits of an organism submitted to an unfavorable environment would not be inherited for long but would disappear. He was on the edge of formulating a theory of the survival of the fittest, though it was adaptation to an environment rather than ability to win out in the struggle for existence conceived as conflict with other individuals. One might phrase his concept of the organism's problem as fitness for survival in a possibly hostile environment. And since within the human environment there are always other people, and since men always dislike those who seem monstrous or dangerous to them, there will be an enforced separation of kinds, the giants going to Patagonia, the blacks to the equatorial regions, the dwarfs towards the Arctic. Thus the psychological desires of a people may isolate members of a tribe and in consequence determine the fixation of certain characters. The matter was complicated, however, as was to happen so frequently in the Occident, by the Biblical story of Adam and Eve. If they formed a primordial couple from whom all mankind has descended, then they must have contained in their seminal fluids the potentialities of a tremendous variety, variety that actually came out in the offspring and was perpetuated by breeding and the influence of the environment.

If I have dealt almost exclusively with the "Earthly Venus" in this Introduction, it is because that book forms the bulk of Maupertuis's ideas on genetics. There is no volume in English that does full justice to his career. Professor Bentley Glass's two essays on "Maupertuis, Pioneer of Genetics and Evolution," and "Heredity and Variation in the Eighteenth Century," tell the story better than any other studies that I have been able to find, but for a full account of the life and works of this scientist one must go to Brunet's thesis, which has been already mentioned. Though the man was accused by his adversaries of being a purely metaphysical dreamer, and was unjustly depreciated by historians, he did make empirical observations on breeding and, as I hope I have made clear, was well read in the works of his biological colleagues. He was one of those men whose ideas were taken up and developed at greater length by scientists of a later age, and Professor Glass in the two studies cited has shown with the authority of a practicing geneticist what fruitfulness was in them. He succeeded in destroying two of the most generally accepted errors of his time, and did so on the whole by simple reasoning. What survived of his own theory was his insistence on the contributions of both parents to the characters of their offspring. This may seem self-evident, but then everything does once it has been demonstrated. Even the great Harvey was hypnotized by the theories of Aristotle, and his theory of generation added next to nothing to the "De generatione animalium" of the Greek. As Professor Joseph Needham says of Maupertuis, "His opinions have an extremely modern ring, and his only retrograde step was in suggesting that the spermatic animal had nothing else to do except to mix the two seeds by swimming about in them."[8] I trust that this brief introduction has sufficiently emphasized the modern ring without falling into the error of lifting him out of his time and place.

George Boas

[8] Joseph Needham, "A History of Embryology," p. 197. Cambridge, 1934.

Part One

Concerning the Origin of Animals

Chapter One. *Introduction*

Only a short while ago did we receive the life which we are to lose. Placed as we are between two moments, that of our birth and that of our death, we try in vain to prolong our being beyond these boundaries. The course of wisdom would be to set our minds only upon doing well by the time between. Being unable to lengthen our lives, both pride and curiosity want to make up for this lack by making ours the time which is to come after us as well as the time which preceded us. Vain hope! But to this is added a new illusion. We imagine that one of these periods is ours more than the other. With only slight curiosity about the past, we avidly question those who promise some knowledge of the future. Men have more easily persuaded themselves that after death they must appear before the Court of Rhadamanthus rather than believe in having fought against Menelaus, before birth, at the siege of Troy.[1] However, the same obscurity dims the future as the past, and if both are considered with philosophical detachment, the interest should remain alike. Anger at dying too soon is not more rational than the complaint of having been born too late.

Without the light of Religion turned upon our being, it would seem that the time before our birth and that

---

[1] Pythagoras remembered the different stages he had gone through before becoming Pythagoras. First, he had been Aethalides; then Euphorbus, wounded by Menelaus before Troy: Hermotinus; the fisherman Pyrrhus; and finally Pythagoras. [See Diogenes Laertius, Book VIII, Section 3.—A.]

following our death constitute two impenetrable abysses whose obscurity is the same for the greatest Philosophers as for people of a crude state of civilization. Therefore, it is not as a Metaphysician that I intend to approach these problems, but only as an Anatomist. More lofty spirits will have to enlighten you, if they can, on the nature of your soul and its origin. I shall only try to let you determine the origin of your body and the different states through which you have gone before reaching the present one. Do not be angry if I say you were a worm, or an egg, or even a kind of mud. Also do not feel that all is lost in losing the form now attained when this body, full of charm, is reduced to ashes.

Nine months after a woman has surrendered to the pleasure which perpetuates humankind, she brings into the world a small creature different from man only in its proportions and the weakness of its various parts. Inside pregnant women who died before giving birth, the child has been found wrapped in a double membrane attached by a cord to the mother's abdomen. The child's resemblance to a man in size and figure is in inverse proportion to the length of time before birth. Seven or eight months before birth the embryo has been found to have a human face, and attentive mothers have already felt some movement.

Before this it is only formless matter. The young wife may hope to have an old husband find in it both the proof of his tenderness and of the heir of which a fatal accident has deprived him. The parents of a young girl see this mass as only blood and lymph, the cause of the languor noticed for some time.

Are these the beginnings of our being? How did the

child found in the mother's womb grow there? Where did it come from? Is this one of the impenetrable mysteries or can the observations of Natural Philosophers throw light on these questions?

I shall now explain the different systems that have divided Philosophers concerning the means of generation. Nothing shall be said to alarm your modesty. But do not let ridiculous prejudices arouse a sense of indecency about a subject which has none in itself. Seduction, perjury, jealousy, or superstition must not disgrace humanity's most important act, even if at times they precede or follow it.

Man lives in a state of melancholy that makes him find everything insipid until the moment when he discovers the person who is to bring him happiness. At her sight all becomes beautiful in his eyes; he breathes a sweeter and purer air; solitude keeps fresh the idea of the loved one; he finds in a crowd good reason for self-congratulation in his choice; all nature attends what he loves. He feels a renewed ardor for all undertakings and in each there is a new promise of success. She who has charmed him becomes imbued with the same fire and surrenders. As she gives herself over to his transports, the happy lover surveys rapidly the many aspects of the beauty by which he has become dazzled and the most delectable becomes his. O wretched men, who by a wicked knife have been deprived of this knowledge! To have the thread of your days cut would have been less fatal. In spite of living in great palaces, wandering within delightful gardens, and possessing all the riches of Asia, the meanest of your slaves able to experience the above pleasures is far happier than you. You, who have been sacrificed to luxurious kings by avaricious parents, are nothing but sinister shadows and empty voices. You may moan and weep over your sorrows, but never sing of love.

It is that moment, so rich in delight, which brings to life a new being capable of understanding the most exalted subjects and, what is far better, who will share similar pleasures.

How explain this transformation? How describe the site of man's first abode? How will this blissful area become a dark prison for a formless and senseless embryo? How can it be that the cause of such pleasure, the origin of so perfect a being, is nothing more than flesh and blood?[2]

Let us not tarnish these facts with repulsive descriptions. Let them remain behind their protective veil. Only the membrane of the maidenhead shall be torn. The doe will take Iphigenia's place and female animals will serve our researches on generation. We shall examine their entrails to discover what we can about this mystery, and, if necessary, we shall turn to the birds and insects.

---

[2] Miseret atque etiam pudet aestimantem quam sit frivola animantium superbissimi origo. Pliny, "Natural History," Book VII, Chap. 7. ["It is pitiful and indeed shameful to think how trivial is the origin of the proudest of living beings!"—A.]

Chapter Two. *Theories of Generation among the Ancients*

At the end of a canal which Anatomists call the *vagina,* the Latin word for sheath, there is found the womb, or uterus. It is a kind of closed pouch with only a small orifice into the vagina that can open or shut and looks pretty much like the mouth of a tench. Because of this resemblance some Anatomists have given it that name. The inside of the pouch is lined with a puckered membrane that permits dilatation as the fetus grows in size. This membrane also has many small perforations through which, most likely, is exuded the fluid secreted by the female during intercourse.

The Ancients believed that the embryo originated from the mixture of the seminal fluids given off by both sexes. That of the male, when propelled into the womb, combined with that of the female. After this mingling had taken place, the Ancients found no difficulty in understanding the creation of an animal. The operation was due to the *Generative Force.*

Aristotle, as may well be believed, was not more puzzled than others by the problem of generation. He differed only in believing that the generative principle came solely from the male. The female fluid's only function was providing food and growth for the fetus. To use Aristotle's terms, it supplied the matter while the male supplied the form.[3]

---

[3] Aristotle, "De generatione animalium," Book II, Chap. 4. ["While it is necessary for the female to provide a body and a material mass, it is not necessary for the male. . . . While the body is from the female, it is the soul that is from the male, for the soul is the reality"—that is, the form or final cause—"of a particular body." Arthur Platt, trans., p. 738b. Oxford Univ. Press, 1910.—A.]

Chapter Three. *The Theory of Ovism*

During many centuries the explanation above satisfied Philosophers for, in spite of a few differences in the interpretation of the functions of the two fluids, they all stopped there and attributed to the mixture the great principle of generation.

New anatomical researches brought to light two whitish bodies around the uterus. These consisted of several round vesicles filled with a fluid similar to the white of egg. The similarity as soon as it was noted became law and these bodies were regarded as having the same function as ovaries in birds and the vesicles were regarded as true eggs. But since the ovaries were placed outside the uterus, how could the eggs, even if they were detached from them, be carried into the cavity where the fetus grows, though one would grant that it is not formed there? Fallopius found two tubes whose floating extremities, in the abdomen, have a kind of fringe which may reach over the ovary, receive the egg, and then propel it to the uterus into which these tubes open.

At this time Natural Philosophy was taking a new turn. A desire to understand all and the belief that this was possible were in the air. No longer were the scholars satisfied by the theory that the embryo was formed by the mingling of two fluids. Various examples in nature, available to all eyes, brought to mind that perhaps the embryo was contained and already formed in each egg. What had been taken for a new production was simply the natural development of their parts made known by their growth. All fecundity then fell to the females. The eggs destined to produce males each contained only one male. But the egg from which a female was to be born contained not only that one, who was complete with her own ovaries in which other females were also contained, just as completely formed, so that the source of generation was assured *ad infinitum*. All these females, contained one within the other, always diminishing in size in relation to the first, only alarm one's imagination. Since matter is infinitely divisible, the embryo formed in its egg, to be born in a thousand years, can be formed as accurately as the one to be born in nine months. Hidden from us by its smallness, it is in no way prevented from obeying the same laws that cause the oak seen in the acorn to develop and spread its branches over the earth.

However, though men are all formed within the eggs from mother to mother, they are lifeless. They are as small figures one inside the other, as are those clever boxes fashioned in wood on a lathe and fitted one inside the other until all are contained in the biggest. In order to make men out of these small statues, a new subtle substance must enter their limbs, creating movement, growth, and life. This is known as the seminal spirits provided by the male in the fluid given off with so much pleasure. Is that not the fire sung by poets as having been stolen from the gods by Prometheus to give men souls and make them free to act? And should not the gods be jealous of that theft?

In order to explain how this fluid, propelled into the vagina, is to fertilize the egg, the simplest idea first comes to mind. The fluid, it is maintained, flows into the womb through the latter's orifice, which opens to receive it. From the womb the more vital portion of the fluid then reaches the tubes and ascends through them to the ovaries that they overlay at the time. Then the egg to be fertilized absorbs the fluid.

This opinion, although rather likely, met several objections.

The fluid emptied into the vagina, far from seeming to penetrate further, slips back as everyone knows.

Many stories are told about young women having become pregnant without the insertion of the organ which is to sow the seed into the vagina, but merely by having allowed the fluid to be spread over its edge. These so-called facts are dubious, as no scientist has been able to check them, and only the word of the women remains, frequently lacking in truthfulness concerning this subject. It would seem that there is surer proof that it is not necessary for the male's seed to enter the womb in order to make the female pregnant. Many animals' uteri, opened after intercourse, show none of this fluid.

It cannot be asserted that the fluid never enters the womb. A famous Anatomist, Verheyen,[4] found an abundant quantity in the uterus of a heifer that had just been bred. And though such examples are few, one of them is better proof that the male fluid does enter the womb than a multitude of cases in which none has been found.

Those who believe that the seed does not enter the womb hold that once in the vagina or only spread on its edges it reaches the small blood vessels which absorb the substance through their tiny mouths and then scatter it

[4] Philippe Verheyen, 1648–1710, author of a book on human anatomy entitled "Corporis humani anatomia," Louvain, 1693.—A.

throughout the female's blood stream. Soon it becomes well mixed with the blood and causes all the miseries that torment women in early pregnancy. Finally the blood's circulation carries the seed to the ovary and the egg is at last fertilized, but only, it would seem, after all the female's blood has become fecund.

Whatever the manner of the egg's fertilization, whether by immediate contact with the male's seed and rapid penetration, or through the roundabout means of the circulation of the blood into which it had become absorbed, it is this seed or seminal spirit that is responsible for touching off motion and growth in the tiny but formed embryo. The egg, until then firmly attached to the ovary, leaves it and slips down into the tube whose extremity encircles the ovary in order to receive it. Continuing its progress down the whole length of the tube, the egg reaches the womb either through its own momentum or, more likely, due to some peristaltic motion within the tube. Like the seeds of plants and trees in fertile soil, the egg then sends out roots which penetrate the womb, forming a masslike substance called the placenta. On the upper surface a long cord develops and is joined to the navel of the fetus. This carries to him the essences necessary for his growth from the mother's blood until he no longer needs it. At such a time the blood vessels that bind the placenta to the womb dry up and wither away, leaving the walls of the womb. The child, at this point having enough strength and ready to face birth, tears the double membrane which has enveloped him, just as the chick breaks the eggshell when it has reached the time of hatching. The type of hardness which is characteristic of birds' eggshells does not make the comparison between the child enclosed in his wrappings and the young bird in his egg impossible. The eggs of various animals, such as those of snakes, lizards, and fish, do not have a hard shell but are covered with a softish flexible material. The analogy is confirmed and brought even closer by the generation of certain animals, termed viviparous, and that of the oviparous. In the females' bodies are found both eggs and little ones already free of their enveloping membrane.[5] Some find that the eggs of several animals ·hatch only long after they have left the body of the female parent, while others hatch before. Though nature seems to indicate various forms of generation, do they not come to the same thing in the end?

[5] *Mémoires de l'Académie des Sciences* **1727**, Tome II, p. 32. [This reference is to an early work of Maupertuis himself, "Observations et Expériences sur une des espèces de Salamandre" ("Observations and Experiments on a Species of Salamander"). He says in this report that he opened some salamanders and to his surprise found both eggs and young "as perfect as those of viviparous animals," p. 44.—A.]

Chapter Four. *Doctrine of Spermatic Animals*

Physicists and Anatomists, easily pleased by any system, found the above completely acceptable. They believed that the tiny embryo was already formed within the female's egg before any intervention of the male, as firmly as if they had seen it. What imagination saw in the egg, the eyes perceived somewhere else. A young Scientist, Hartsoeker,[6] took it upon himself to examine under a microscope the fluid which is not usually the object of attentive and critical eyes. What a marvelous sight when he discovered live creatures! One drop became an ocean filled with a multitude of tiny fish swimming in all directions. He tried the same experiment with similar fluids from various animals and in each always came upon the wonderful sight, numberless living animals, but of different shapes. This led to the examination of the blood and all other body fluids in search of some similar phenomenon. Nothing was found, no matter how powerful the microscope. The seas remained free of any living creature.

There was no difficulty in thinking that the little animals found in the male's seminal fluid were the ones that one day would reproduce him. In spite of their infinitely

[6] Nicolas Hartsoeker, 1656–1725, author of a book on what today would be called genetics, the "Conjectures physiques," Amsterdam, 1706; an "Essai de dioptrique," 1694; and "Principes de physique," 1696. He discovered the spermatozoa with a microscope of his own make and disclosed his findings to Huyghens. Huyghens took him to Paris where he made friends with Cassini. Meanwhile the spermatozoa had already been seen by Johann Ham, assistant to van Leeuwenhoek, in 1677.—A.

small size and their fishlike form, the Scientists could easily conceive of their change on both counts, as nature was known frequently to bring this about. Thousands of examples of complete change are known to us where there is no resemblance between the final development of the animal and its appearance at birth. Who could recognize the small worm as being the same as the fully grown June bug, without constant watching? And who could believe that the brilliantly colored winged insects seen flying about at night were small creatures crawling in the mud or swimming in water?

Now here was fecundity, formerly attributed to the females, given back to the males! The tiny worm, swimming in seminal fluid, became the agent responsible for an infinite number of generations carried on from father to father. Furthermore it was conceived as having its own seminal substance in which swam proportionately smaller animals, and so on indefinitely. This concept becomes truly prodigious when the size and numbers of the small animals are considered! On this ground it was figured that during its first generation the seminal fluid of one pike could produce more pikes than there are men on earth, assuming the density of population to be generally that of Holland. When future generations are considered, we are overcome by unfathomable depths of number and tininess. From one generation to the next the bodies of these minuscule animals grow smaller in a scale running from man's size to that of those atomies seen only under the best microscope. Their numbers increase as from unity to the fabulous number of creatures scattered in this fluid.

What tremendous riches and fecundity without end! Has not nature become too lavish? Is not the display and the outlay excessive? From this multitude of tiny creatures swimming in the seminal substance usually only one reaches the human state. Seldom do women, though well impregnated, give birth to twins and practically never to triplets. Although animals bear larger numbers, even then the number born is to all intents and purposes nil in comparison with the multitude swimming in the seminal fluid spilled by the male. What useless waste!

To know which is to nature's greatest credit—precise economy or superfluous profusion—it would be necessary to understand her designs or rather the designs of Him Who governs her. We have, however, before our eyes many examples of the same profusion in the reproduction of trees and plants. How many millions of acorns fall from an oak to dry up or rot, as compared to the very small number that germinate and become trees! But may we not see that this great quantity of acorns was not useless, for if the one which germinated had not fallen, there would have been no reproduction and no new generation?

By using this multitude of useless seminal animals, a chaste and religious Physicist, Leeuwenhoek, carried out numerous experiments, none of which, we are told, were made at the expense of his family. These animals have a tail and look much like the frog at birth when it still has the shape of the little black fishes called tadpoles wiggling in the spring freshets. The former, at first, show great activity, but as the fluid in which they swim cools or evaporates, they slow down and finally perish. Many more die within the area where they are put, becoming lost in its labyrinth. But what of the one destined to become a man? Which path does he follow? What transforms him into an embryo?

Only some imperceptible areas of the uterus's inner

membrane are able to receive the little animal and give him the juices necessary for his growth. In women's wombs these particular areas are scarcer than in the uteri of animals able to bear several young. The single spermatic animal or animals finding such niches will adhere to the membrane by a special web which will become the placenta. Thus uniting with the mother's body, the fibers will carry to these particular spermatic animals what nourishment is needed. The others will perish like seed sown in arid soil, for the uterus is to them a vast area, and several thousands die without having found the little cavities destined to receive them.

As we try to understand the changes undergone by the small animal while confined in the uterus, we might compare him to other animals that go through just as important changes right under our eyes. In fact, while transformations still are worthy of our admiration, they should no longer cause us any surprise. Butterflies and many other similar creatures begin by being a type of worm. One of these lives on leaves, another is underground and eats roots. After having reached a certain stage in this form, they take on a new one. Now one may appear sealed in a case constricting and hiding the various parts of its body in such a way that it no longer looks like a living animal. Those who raise silkworms call it the *fève* (bean). The naturalists call it a chrysalis because of the few golden spots which sometimes decorate it. At this time the worm is in a state of immobility and deep lethargy, with all living functions suspended. But as soon as the right time comes, he breaks open the chrysalis, stretches himself, opens his wings, and becomes a butterfly or a similar creature.

Some of these insects, which are so feared by the young

beauties who stroll in the woods, or the ones seen flying on long wings over streams, were originally tiny fish that spent the first part of their lives in water. They left their first environment only upon reaching their final form.

These various stages, which have been taken by clumsy scientists as real metamorphoses, are only skin deep. The butterfly was already completely formed such as we see him fly about our gardens, and only disguised as a caterpillar.

Can we now compare the little animal swimming in the seminal fluid to the caterpillar or the worm? Is the fetus in his mother's womb, wrapped up in his double membrane, a kind of chrysalis? And does he leave it to come forth in his definitive form as the insect does?

From caterpillar to butterfly and from the spermatic worm to man we seem to find a kind of analogy. But here we run into difficulty. The first stage of the butterfly was not the caterpillar, for the latter had already come out of an egg, and that egg may have been only a kind of chrysalis. If the analogy had to be pushed back completely, the tiny spermatic animal must have come from an egg, but what egg? How small could it have been? It is not the size, however, that is our stumbling block.

Chapter Five. *Intermediate System*

Most Anatomists have adopted a new theory, which comes out of the two preceding ones and combines the spermatic animalcules and the eggs. The following explains it.

Life's entire vital principle resides in the small animal containing the whole of man, but the egg is still necessary as being the nutritive mass providing for his food and growth. Among the crowds of animalcules placed in the vagina or projected into the uterus there is one, luckier or more to be pitied than the others, which, swimming or crawling in the fluid soaking these parts, reaches the mouth of the tube which leads him up to the ovary. There he finds an egg ready for him, and having pierced it, he beds himself down to begin the first stage of his growth. In much the same way various insects penetrate fruits that will give them food. The pierced egg then leaves the ovary and falls through the tube into the uterus, to which the small animal becomes attached by the fibers forming the placenta.

Chapter Six. *Observations for and against Eggs*

In the *Mémoires de l'Académie Royale des Sciences* **1701,** p. 109, are found certain statements very favorable to the theory of the egg, either as the container of the fetus, even before fecundation, or later as its first home and source of food.

The description given by M. Littre[7] of the ovary that he dissected deserves close attention. Having found one egg in the tube, he noticed a scar on the surface of the ovary which, he said, was caused by the expulsion of the egg. But none of this is so remarkable as the fetus which he insists he perceived inside an egg, still attached to the ovary.

If the report were absolutely sure, much would have been proved about eggs. But even the *History of the Academy* of the same year makes it doubtful by honestly setting against it M. Méry's[8] observations which lessen its validity.

[7] Alexis Littre, 1658–1725, was the author of the article referred to, the title of which was "Observations sur les ovaires et les trompes d'une femme et sur un foetus trouvé dans l'un de ses ovaires" ("Observations on the ovaries and the tubes of a woman and upon a fetus found in one of her ovaries"). In 1702 he published a second article, entitled "Observations sur un foetus trouvé dans la trompe gauche de la matrice" ("Observations on a fetus found in the left tube of the uterus"). He is credited with having demonstrated the possibility of an extrauterine pregnancy. He did not, however, discover the ovum, but mistook the Graafian follicle for one. Thus when Maupertuis denies the existence of an egg, he was denying that which was wrongly supposed to be one. The mistake was general among the ovists.—A.

[8] Jean Méry (1645–1722), author among other works of "Description exacte de l'oreille de l'homme" ("Exact description of the human ear"),

As against one scar found by M. Littre on the surface of one ovary, he found so many more on a woman's ovary that if they were caused by the ejection of eggs, this would have implied an unheard of fecundity. What is even of greater importance is that Méry found within the uterus's thick membrane a vesicle entirely similar to the ones referred to as eggs.

Although observations made by M. Littre and other Anatomists show that they have at times found fetuses in the tubes, this proves nothing concerning the fetus. No matter how it is formed, it has to be found within the uterus's cavity, and the tubes are only a part of this cavity.

M. Méry is far from being the only Anatomist to have doubts about women's eggs as well as of those of other viviparous animals. Many scientists consider them pure fantasy. They are unwilling to recognize as true eggs the vesicles which make up the mass which others take for an ovary. The eggs sometimes found in the tubes or even in the uterus are, as far as they are concerned, nothing but some types of hydatids.

Experiments should have solved these problems if in the natural sciences anything were ever solved. Graaf, an Anatomist who carried out a wide range of experiments on female rabbits, dissected them at stated intervals after breeding. He said that after twenty-four hours he found some changes in the ovaries. At a later time the eggs showed greater alterations. Then there were eggs in the

---

1677, and "Nouveau système de la circulation du sang par le trou ovale dans le foetus humain" ("New theory of the circulation of the blood by the foramen ovale in the human fetus"), 1700. Méry maintained against Littre that what was in the ovary was simply little cells filled with a kind of liquid.—A.

tubes and later still, inside the opened females, eggs were found in the uterus. Finally he stated that he had always seen vestiges in the ovaries of the number of eggs found in the tubes or in the uterus.[9]

However, another Anatomist, Verheyen,[10] as exact and conscientious, but prejudiced against the theory of eggs and even of the prolific eggs containing the fetus before fecundation, tried the same experiments without success. He noted alterations or scars on the ovaries but was mistaken when he tried to judge the number of embryos in the uterus according to them.

[9] Regnerus de Graaf, "De Mulierum organis" ("On women's organs").

[10] Philippe Verheyen, 1648–1710, also wrote a well-known treatise entitled "Corporis humani anatomia," Louvain, 1693. This was a general anatomy. In the book cited by Maupertuis, which I have not been able to consult, he apparently denied that the corpora lutea corresponded to the number of the embryos.—A.

Chapter Seven. *Harvey's Experiments*

All these brilliant and likely systems, just examined, would seem ruined by the earlier and weighty judgments made by the great man to whom the study of anatomy owes more than to any other because of his discovery of the circulation of the blood.

Charles I, King of England, was an inquisitive prince and interested in Science. In order to give his Anatomist the possibility of discovering generation's mystery, he turned over to him the does and stags from the royal parks. Harvey carried on a scholarly massacre. Have his experiments thrown any light on the problem of generation? Or, on the contrary, did they not becloud the issue?

Every day Harvey sacrificed to the progress of Science a few does at the time of mating. He dissected their uteri and, examining all those parts with the most attentive eyes, found nothing similar to what Graaf said he had observed. Neither did he find anything favoring any of the systems we have been studying.

Harvey never found any male seminal fluid in the uterus; never any eggs in the tubes; never an alteration in the supposed ovary that he calls, as several other Anatomists did, the female testicle.

The first changes that he found in the organs connected with generation were in the uterus which was swollen and softer [than before copulation]. In quadrupeds it looks as if it were double, while it really has only one cavity. The bottom of the uterus is composed of two hollows that the Anatomists call the *horns* and in them are found the embryos. These areas were the most altered parts. Harvey found there several spongy excrescences [uterine glands] that he compares to the nipples of women. He sliced some and found in them a sprinkling of small white dots coated with a viscous matter. The bottom of the uterus to which they adhered was swollen and tumescent as a child's lips which had been stung by bees. The area seemed so soft that it resembled in consistency the brain. After several years of constant experiments on does during September and October, which is the daily breeding time, Harvey found nothing more. He never discovered a drop of seminal fluid in all these opened uteri, for he insists that he made sure that a purulent substance, found in a few twenty days after breeding, was not the same.

When he reported his findings to others, they suggested, and perhaps he also had feared it, that the dissected does had not been actually impregnated. In order to convince the skeptics, or to make sure, he had twelve does closed in a paddock after the rutting season. He then opened up a few of these, in which he found no more vestiges of the male's seed than previously. The remaining does bore their fawns. From the results of all these experiments and of many others, carried out with rabbits, bitches, and other animals, Harvey concluded that the male's seed does not remain in and possibly may not even enter the uterus.

By November the tumescence of the uterus had diminished and the spongy caruncles had become flaccid. But what was entirely new were filaments stretched from one horn of the uterus to the other, forming a kind of webbing similar to that made by spiders. Working their way in and out of the wrinkles of the uterus's inner membrane, they wove themselves around the caruncles much as the *pia mater* follows and covers the contours of the brain.

Soon a pouch was formed by this network, the outside of which was coated with fetid matter, while the inside, smooth and polished, contained a substance similar to the white of egg. In this floated another sphere, filled with clearer crystalline fluid. It was in the latter that a new wonder was discovered: not a well-organized animal, as previous systems had led us to believe, but the animal principle, that is, a "capering bloody point,"[11] before any of its future parts were formed. It was seen in the crystalline fluid jumping and pulsating, drawing its substance from a vein lost in this liquid. When Harvey showed it to the King, exposed to the sun, it was still pulsating.

Soon the various parts of the body took shape, but in varying order and at different times. At first there was only a mucilaginous substance divided in two small areas, one of which became the head and the other the trunk. Towards the end of November the fetus was formed and this admirable development, once begun, was soon finished. Eight days after the first sign of life, the animal had made such progress that its sex became known. But again this came about only bit by bit, and the inner parts were formed before the external ones, the viscera and intestines coming into being before they were encased in the thorax and abdomen. These last parts, destined to protect the earlier ones, were finally added as the roof is added to a building.

Until then no adherence of the fetus to the mother's

[11] This is the punctum saliens. For the place of this in the history of embryology, see Joseph Needham, "A History of Embryology," p. 115. Cambridge, 1934. The English phrase is Harvey's.—A.

body was evident. The membrane containing the crystalline fluid in which the small animal swam, called *amnion*
by Anatomists, was itself suspended in the liquid contained in the *chorion,* the membrane that was first formed.
All of this was held within the uterus without any
adhesions.

By the beginning of December the use of the spongy
caruncles [the uterine glands] was discovered. These were
mentioned earlier as occurring on the inner wall of the
uterus and resembled female teats. The caruncles were
then only glued to the embryo's envelope by the muci-
lage that they contained, but soon became more firmly
held by the reception of blood vessels from the fetus. In
so doing they served as a base to the placenta.

All that remained to achieve were varying degrees of
growth, which the fetus attained each day. Finally when
it reached the period of birth, it ruptured the membranes
which enveloped it and the placenta left the uterus. The
animal coming out of its mother's body saw then the
light of day. The female animals bite off the umbilical
cord of blood vessels that ties the fetus to the placenta,
thus destroying a connection that is no longer useful. Mid-
wives tie this cord and cut it.

These are Harvey's observations. They seem so at
variance with the system of the egg and that of the spermatic animals, I feared if stated before the latter, they
would have prejudiced the reader completely against them
and would have prevented any attentive reading.

Instead of seeing the animal grow through the intus-
susception of new matter, as it must be if it were formed
inside the female's egg or if it were the small worm
swimming in the male's spermatic fluid, here we have an

animal formed by the juxtaposition of new parts. Harvey first saw the pouch being formed to hold the new being, and this pouch, instead of being the membrane of an egg which would become dilated, was being made under his eyes like the weaving of a piece of linen. At first there were only webs stretched from one end of the uterus to the other and as they multiplied and were drawn closer, they then formed a genuine membrane. The formation of this envelope, a true marvel, should prepare us for others.

Harvey says nothing of the formation of the inner membrane that he probably did not witness, but he did see the animal swimming in it in the process of growth. At first it was a mere point, but a living one around which other parts grouped themselves in order soon to form an animal.[12]

---

[12] Guillelm. Harvey, *De Cervarum & Damarum coitu.* Exercit. LXVI.

Chapter Eight. *Harvey's Views of Generation*

The many experiments spoken of above, deeply opposed to the system of eggs and of the spermatic animals, seemed to Harvey the destruction of the system based on a joining of the two seeds, because these two were not found in the uterus. As a result this great man, unable to give a clear and lucid explanation of generation, found himself reduced to comparisons. Consequently he says that the female is made pregnant by the male as iron acquires a magnetic character after having been touched by a magnet. From this comparison he launches into an analysis far more scholastic than scientific and ends up by comparing the fecund uterus to the brain, the substance of which it imitates. *The former conceives the embryo just as the latter conceives ideas.* What a strange account and how frustrating to those wishing to penetrate into nature's secrets!

Such results are nearly always the outcome of most profound research. A satisfying system is erected while the characteristics of the phenomenon under study are ignored. As soon as they are brought to light, the superficiality of the reasoning is evident and the system collapses. Whenever we assume knowledge, it is because of deep ignorance. Our mind seems to be destined to reason only from facts discovered by our senses. Microscopes and glasses have, as it were, provided us with new senses quite beyond our own normal capacities. They should belong rightfully to higher intelligences and often confuse our limited faculties.

Chapter Nine. *Attempts to Reconcile Observations with Ovism*

Would it be permissible to alter slightly Harvey's observations? Could they be interpreted in such a way as to bring them closer to the system of ovism or that of the spermatic worms? Could one believe that some facts might have escaped this great man? Such a fact might be that an egg freed from the ovary fell into the uterus while the first envelope was being formed, and became wrapped in it. The second membrane might then be the egg's very own, containing the little embryo. This might even be there before fecundation, as is believed by those who believe eggs to be prolific, or it might have entered the egg in the shape of a worm. But can we accept the idea that Harvey was mistaken in all that he tells us of the embryo's formation? Could the existence of preformed limbs have escaped him because of their soft and transparent nature? Could he have taken them for newly added parts while they were only becoming more noticeable through their growth? The first envelope, which Harvey saw as a pouch being formed, would still be embarrassing. Could its original formation have escaped the Anatomist, or might it have come from the viscous matter oozing out of the uterus's "nipple" as skin is formed on milk?

Chapter Ten. *Attempts to Reconcile These Observations with the Theory of Spermatic Animalcules*

If the aim´were to bring Harvey's observations closer to the theory of the vermicules, it might be conceded that although, as he maintained, the fluid itself which carries them does not enter the uterus, it would be easy enough for some of them to enter as its orifice opens into the vagina. Why not propose as a theory one which might seem too bold to ordinary Anatomists but which could not surprise those who are used to observe the habits of insects? It is the most easily applicable here. Might not the little worm introduced into the uterus have woven the membrane forming the first envelope? Either it might have produced the filaments which Harvey first detected, from one side of the uterus to the other, or it might have simply organized in this manner the viscous matter that was found. We have examples among insects that support this idea. Several insects, when at the point of metamorphosis, begin by spinning or producing out of a foreign substance a covering for themselves. Thus the silkworm constructs its cocoon. It soon sheds its worm's skin as well as that which succeeds it and is then replaced by the chrysalis within which his various parts are encased and where it remains until ready to emerge as a butterfly.

Our spermatic animalcule, after having woven its first casing, which corresponds to the silk cocoon, would then shut itself in it and strip itself down to the state of a chrysalis, that is, within a second casing which would be only one of its skins. The crystalline liquid contained inside the second membrane and in which appears the animated point [punctum saliens], would be the actual body of the animal, but transparent as crystal and of so soft a consistency as to be fluid. Such an organic structure could have been misread by Harvey. The sea often washes on the sands jellylike and transparent substances that do not seem much more of an organism than the matter we speak of and yet they are genuine animals. The embryo's first enclosing membrane, the chorion, would be its own product; the second, the amnion, would be its skin.

Have we the right to doubt such authentic observations and thus sacrifice them to analogies and theories? Again, in dealing with things so difficult to observe, is it not possible that some may have escaped the most diligent of observers?

Chapter Eleven. *Variety among Animals*

Analogy frees our mind from having to imagine new things and from an even greater worry, that of remaining uncertain. It pleases our mind, but does it please nature as much?

Undoubtedly some similarity exists between the means known to be used by various species of animals in reproducing themselves. In spite of nature's infinite variety, changes never come suddenly. Because of ignorance we may well take as closely related, species which are far enough apart so that the similarities previously noted, and now looked for, are either lost or unrecognized.

In fact, what a variety is to be found in the means that different species have of reproducing themselves!

The impetuous bull, proud of his strength, wastes no time in endearments, but instantly springs upon the heifer, penetrates her deeply, and discharges in a stream substance that must fecundate her.

By a series of tender cooings, the turtle doves make known their love and thousands of kisses and playful gestures precede the last act.

An insect with long wings[13] flies in the sky in pursuit of his mate. When he reaches her, they embrace and, becoming linked together, the two lovers fly away, carried on the winds in carefree abandon.[14]

[13] The dragon fly, *Perla* in Latin.

[14] Maupertuis here refers to the "Mémoires" of Réaumur but fails to indicate the edition he uses. I have checked his references in the edition published in Paris in 1740 and here, as hereafter, cite that edition. The reference at this point should be to Vol. VI, p. 420.—A.

Certain creatures, long misjudged and known as galls, are far from being able to give their love such an airing. The female with a shape so unlike an animal spends most of her life in immobility, fixed to the surface of a tree. She is encased in a sort of scaly surface which completely hides her body. An almost imperceptible slit is the only opening to life for this animal. The male of this strange creature is completely unlike her, being a gnat. His infidelities are unknown to her and his caresses are patiently awaited. After the insertion of the winged creature's organ in the slit, the female becomes so fecund that it would seem as if her outer scaly skin were a pouch filled with innumerable little ones.

The insect gall is not the only species of which the male flies in the air while the wingless female, of completely different aspect, crawls on the ground. The diamonds, sparkling in the shrubbery in the autumn nights, are glow-worms, females of winged insects that would literally lose them in the darkness if not guided by their mates' little torches.[15]

Shall I mention animals whose form prompts scorn and revulsion? Yes, but nature has not treated them as a harsh stepmother. The toad holds his mate in an embrace for months.

While so many animals are full of eagerness in their amorous pursuits, the timid fish conducts himself with extreme reticence. He does not dare approach the female nor even touch her, but only forlornly follows her in the waters, finding his happiness in fertilizing her eggs, once she has dropped them.

[15] *Histoire de l'Académie des Sciences* **1723**, 9. [The reference is to a report of Réaumur, "Sur la lumière des Dails."—A.]

Are these animals' generative operations completely un-
selfish or is the considerate nature of their feelings a
happy substitute for what they seem to lack? Yes, truly,
for a glance can be a source of delight and anything may
bring happiness to the one who loves. Nature has an
equal interest in perpetuating all species and thus in-
spires each with the same motive. That motive is pleasure,
pleasure which in the human species sweeps everything
before it. In spite of multiple obstacles in the way of a
union of two hearts, and of a thousand torments that
must follow, Nature still leads the lovers to her desired
end.[16]

If fish seem so self-controlled in their love-making, there
are other animals which carry theirs to the most unre-
strained debauchery. The queen bee has a seraglio of
lovers and satisfies them all. In vain does she hide her
private life behind walls; in vain did she overawe the
savant Swammerdam, an illustrious observer,[17] convinced
of her prostitutions through his own eyes. Her fecundity
is equal to her intemperance, for she becomes the mother
to thirty to forty thousand offspring.

The multitude of these colonies is not their most

[16]
Ita capta lepore
Illecebrisque tuis omnis natura animantium,
Te sequitur cupide, quo quamque inducere pergis.
Lucretius, *De rerum natura,* I,15 ff.
["So captivated by thy charms and by thine allurements, all animate
nature follows thee with desire whither thou wishest to lead them."]
Munro in his edition of Lucretius says, "*Illecebrisque* etc. is inserted by
Juntine and in most subsequent editions . . . It has been generally
assigned to Marullus but . . . I assign it to Angelo Politian." For
further details see his note on these verses.—A.

[17] "Histoire des Insectes" of M. de Réaumur. ["Mémoires," Vol. V,
p. 498. Swammerdam thought that the embryo was contained in the
egg but began to grow "after having been vivified by the male."—A.]

wonderful characteristic but rather the fact that they are not limited to two sexes as other animals are. The bee family is composed of a very small number of females, each destined to be queen of a new swarm of about two thousand males and of a prodigious number of neuters, insects without sex. These are unhappy slaves slated to make honey, feed the young as soon as they are born, and to keep up by their labor the luxury and plenitude of the hive.

There comes, however, a time when the slaves rebel against those they have served so well. As soon as the queen's passion has been satisfied, she orders death for the males and leaves them to the fury of the workers. Since they are far more numerous than the males; they carry out a frightful holocaust that ends only when the last male in the swarm has been murdered.

Such is a type of animal far different from those we have previously studied. In the latter the family consisted of two members which were sufficient to produce and care for their young and thus continue the species. In the former the family has only one female, but the male sex seems to be shared by thousands of individuals, and a far greater number of the members have no sex at all.

As a contrast, in certain species we find the two sexes present in each individual. Every snail has both male and female parts. Still they cling to each other; they entwine themselves about each other with the help of long cords which become their generative organs. After this double copulation, each snail lays eggs.

I cannot omit one singular fact concerning these animals. When the time of copulation is near, Nature arms each individual with a small dart made of hard and crus-

taceous matter.[18] Later this dart falls off naturally, probably after it has been used. But what is its use? What
function does this temporary organ serve? Perhaps this
animal, so cold and so slow in all its operations, needs to
be excited by the dart's stings. People who have become
frigid with age or whose senses have lost their acuity have
had recourse to such violent means to awaken their passion.
Poor wretches! who try through pain to excite feelings
which should only arise from voluptuous pleasure, you
had better give in to lethargy and death. Spare yourselves
useless pain, for it is not your blood which gave birth to
Venus, as Tibullus once said.[19]

You should have availed yourselves in time of the means
Nature had provided for your happiness. Had you done so,
you would not now push their use beyond the boundaries
prescribed by time. Instead of irritating the fibers of
your body, console your soul for its losses.

Even so you would be more to be pardoned than the
young man who, driven by a strange mixture of superstition and gallant display, flagellates himself before his
mistress in order to prove to her the torments he can
endure for her, as well as the pleasures to come.

Were I to enumerate all that passion has caused men
to conceive in order to exceed and prolong its enjoyment,
I should never finish. Innocent snail, you are probably
the only one for whom such means are not criminal, for

---

[18] Maupertuis refers here to a work by Heister called "Historia de
Cochleis" ("Natural History of Snails"). I have not been able to
identify this work.—A.

[19]   Is sanguine natam
     Is Venerem et rapido sentiat esse mari. Tibullus, I, ii, 39–40.
["(Every gossip) will know that Venus was born from blood and from
the swirling sea."—A.]

in your case they are the results of Nature's order. Receive and give thousands of stings from the darts that Nature has given you. For us there are only glances and kindly attentions.

In spite of the snails' privilege of possessing both sexes, Nature did not mean that they should not need one another. Two of them are necessary to carry on the species.[20]

But now we come to a perfect hermaphrodite—the common garden insect known as Aphis. Without any copulation it reproduces a fellow creature in giving birth to another live aphis. Such an amazing fact could not be accepted, had it not been seen by the most conscientious naturalists and verified by Monsieur de Réaumur. Nothing in nature escaped him but he also saw only what was there.[21]

An aphis was caught as it emerged from his mother's or father's abdomen and without contact with any other aphis was carefully kept and fed in a closed glass jar. There it was seen to give birth to a great number of aphides. One of these was then taken after birth and the experiment repeated with the same result. Thus five generations, carefully controlled, were produced without copulation. But what might seem to be equally surprising is that these

[20] Mutuis animis, amant, amantur. Catullus, 45, line 20 ["With souls reflecting, they love, they are loved." The preceding line reads, "Nunc ab auspicio bono profecti" ("Now when they have set forth under good auspices . . .")—A.]

[21] Just what species of aphis Maupertuis was discussing is not recorded, but in most species there are two sexes. The female is fertilized in the autumn by a male and proceeds to lay eggs throughout the winter which hatch in the spring. These individuals are females and do produce thousands of young without any further operations of the male. Maupertuis apparently had no information about their sexual union in the autumn and naturally thought that the production of young aphides was parthenogenic.—A.

same aphides, which can breed without copulation, do copulate whenever they wish.[22]

Might it be possible that these animals which produce others while being entirely separate from any of their kind, have copulated in their mother's abdomen or might it be that one copulation could generate several generations? Whatever side is taken and whatever is imagined, nothing analogous is known.

An aquatic worm, called polyp, has even more surprising means of multiplying. As a tree sprouts new branches, a polyp sprouts young polyps. When these have reached a certain size, they drop off, but often, even before leaving the main trunk, they themselves produce new polyps and all these descendants of various generations still hold on to the common ancestor. The worthy author of these discoveries tried to find out whether the natural generation of polyps was anything more than this spontaneous growth, or whether there was some previous copulation. In order to make sure, he employed the most ingenious and careful means of observation and was on his guard against all the wiles of love that the most stupid, as well as the more astute, of animals are known to make use of. The result of all his observations was that the generation of these animals is accomplished without any kind of copulation.

Why should this be surprising when we learn of the polyp's other means of reproduction? Will this be believed when I relate it? It has, however, been found

---

[22] "Histoire des Insectes," by M. de Réaumur [Vol. III, pp. 288 ff. Actually Réaumur (*ibid.*, p. 327) says he has never seen any copulation and that if any occurs, it must be a long time before they are mature. —A.]

constant in experimentation according to accounts that cannot be doubted. In order to multiply itself, one of these animals only needs to be cut in pieces. The part with the head grows a tail, while the end with the tail produces a head, and those parts that have neither head nor tail produce both.

This Hydra, more wonderful than that of the fable, can be split lengthwise or mutilated in every way and soon all is repaired and each part has become a new animal.[23]

What can one think of this strange kind of generation —of this life-giving principle spread throughout the animal? Could these animals be a mass of embryos, all ready for immediate development as soon as given a chance? Or are there unknown means which are able to reproduce what the mutilated parent has lost? Has Nature, which in all other animals has joined pleasure to the act of generation, given these a voluptuous sensation when they are cut in pieces?

[23] *Phil. Trans.* **567.** The work in which M. Trembley gives the public all his discoveries about these animals, will be published. [Abraham Trembley, 1700–1784, was a Swiss who investigated the lives of both the Hydra and Plumatella, among other forms. He seems to have been the first to recognize that these forms were animal and not vegetable. His monograph on the polyp is entitled "Mémoires pour servir à l'histoire d'un polype d'eau douce," Leyden, 1744.—A.]

Chapter Twelve. *Thoughts on Systems of Growth*

Most modern Physicists, guided by the analogy of plant growth, which might seem like the production of new parts, but is really the development of parts already present in the seed or the bulb, could not understand how an organized body might actually be produced. Such scientists wished to reduce all generation to simple development. Consequently they believed that all animals of each kind were already completely formed inside either the father or the mother, thus obviating the necessity of a new reproduction.

Neither the extremely small size of these animals' parts nor the fluidity of the liquids that would have to flow through them would be the cause of my objections. I should ask the Physicists for the permission to examine more deeply their ideas and see whether (1) what is seen in the apparent production of plants is applicable to the generation of animals, and (2) whether that theory of development makes natural science any clearer than the admission of new reproductions.

As to the first of these questions, it is obvious that one sees in a tulip bulb the leaves and flowers already formed, so that its apparent production is only a true development of those parts. Where can one apply this comparison if we seek to compare animals to plants? Only to the animal already formed. Furthermore, the bulb will be only a tulip, and how could it be proved that all the tulips to be born from this one are contained in it? This example of plants, upon which Physicists base so much, proves only that there is a condition for plants during which their future is not yet perceivable to the eye. Only development and growth of its parts are necessary for the plant to become visible. Animals do have a similar state, but it is previous to this that we need to know what they were. Consequently, what certainty can we have about the similarity between plants and animals?

As to the second question, how the theory based on development makes natural science more clearly understood than if new productions were admitted, it remains puzzling. As a fact, when it is most difficult to understand how an organic body, such as an animal, can be formed with each new generation, would it be easier to conceive how an infinite succession of animals, contained in each other, could have been formed at once? This is self-delusion, adopted in the hope of resolving the problem by simply making it more remote. The difficulty remains the same unless it becomes an even greater one to conceive all these highly organized creatures being formed one in the other and all within the first member of the species rather than believing that they are produced successively.

Descartes held the belief, as did the Ancients, that man originated in the mixed fluids emitted by both sexes, due to the laws of motion and fermentation. This great Philosopher, in his treatise "On Man," felt he could explain through these laws the formation of a heart, a brain, a nose, eyes, etc.[24]

---

[24] Descartes, "La Description du Corps Humain: De la formation de l'animal," 1648; *in* "Oeuvres de Descartes," Vol. XI, p. 253. Adam-Tannery, ed. Paris, 1909.—A.

If metaphysical reasons can count for something in such a case, Descartes' ideas on the creation of the embryo through the mixture of the two seminal elements have something eminently worth considering. We have no reason to suspect that he entertained the idea out of respect for the Ancients or because he could think of nothing better.

If we do believe that nature's Creator does not simply leave the creation of animals to laws of motion, and if we do believe that He had first to lend a hand and create all these animals contained in one another, what is gained by thinking He created them all at once? And what has natural science lost by the idea that animals are formed successively? For God, is there any real difference between one moment in time and the next?

Chapter Thirteen. *Reasons Which Prove That Both the Father and the Mother Participate in the Embryo's Production*

If no advantage is found nor a broader simplicity discovered in the belief that animals were already completely formed one in the other before their generation, rather than being successively formed and reproduced, their creation remains so far unexplained. There are, however, potent reasons pointing towards an equal contribution by each sex. The child is born sometimes with the father's features and sometimes with the mother's. It is born with their faults and their habits and seems even to have inherited their tendencies and mental characteristics. In spite of the fact that these similarities are not always recognized, they are observed frequently enough not to be attributed to chance and probably they do occur oftener than they are noticed.

In certain species these likenesses are more easily noted. If a black man marries a white woman, it would seem that the two colors were mixed and that their child is a mulatto with features partially resembling those of his father and of his mother.

In species where there is a wider difference, the alteration in the resulting offspring is even greater. The donkey and the mare produce an animal that is neither donkey nor horse but visibly a composite of both. The alteration is so great that the mule's reproductive organs are useless.

Further experiments on breeds more dissimilar would

probably bring about new monstrosities. Everything con-
curs in indicating that the animal that is born is a
composite of the two generative elements. If all animals
of one species had been previously formed and contained
inside one father or one mother, either in the shape of a
worm or eggs, how could we observe these various resemblances? If the fetus were just the vermicule swimming in the seminal fluid of the father, why would he at
times resemble the mother? If he were nothing but the
mother's egg, what would his face have in common with
his father's?   Could the little colt, already completely
formed within the mare's egg, take on the donkey's ears
because a donkey had set the egg's parts in motion? Will
it ever be believed or imagined that because the spermatic
vermicule has been nourished within the mother, he will
have acquired a resemblance to her and her traits? Would
it be much more ridiculous to think that animals should
resemble the food they eat or the dwellings they live in?

Chapter Fourteen. *Theories Concerning Monsters*

In the *Mémoires de l'Académie des Sciences* there is found a long dispute between two famous men which might never have ended without the death of one of them. The subject concerned monsters. In all species there are often born individuals that are deformed, missing some essential part or having such in excess. The two Anatomists accepted ovism. One insisted that monsters were only the result of some accident or other to the eggs; the other believed that the eggs themselves were at the start monstrous, containing already formed monsters, just as other eggs contained normal animals.

One Scientist explained quite clearly how a certain commotion among the eggs caused the birth of monsters. If some parts of the eggs during their soft period were destroyed by an accident, there would be born a mutilated child—a defective monster. The union or confusion between two eggs or two germs in one egg produced monsters by excess or individuals born with superfluous parts. The simplest form of monster would be twins just attached to each other, such as have been seen at times. In this case no vital part of the egg has been destroyed. Certain superficial parts of the embryos having been torn and brought together again might have caused the adherence of the two bodies. Two-headed monsters or those having one head and two bodies only differ from the former because more parts in one of the eggs were destroyed. In one egg all parts needed for one of the bodies were gone, while in the other it was the part to form one of the heads. Finally, a child having one finger too many is a monster composed from two eggs, one of which has been completely destroyed except for that finger.

The adversary in the argument, who was more anatomically minded than rational, refused to be blinded by the kind of light spread by the above thought and simply objected that the monsters that he himself had dissected seemed not to be explained by any accidental disorder.

The reasoning of one attempted to explain the disorders; the monsters of the other just multiplied. With each explanation that M. de Lemery brought forth, M. de Winslow produced a new monster to put down.[25] Finally they came to metaphysical explanations. One found it scandalous to think that God had created monstrous germs, while the other believed that it put a limit on God's powers to hold him to too great a regularity and uniformity.

Those who might wish to see what has been said during this quarrel can find it in the *Mémoires de l'Académie*.[26]

[25] Lemery, Louis (1697–1743) came from a family of some fame in chemistry, but wrote many articles on physiology and anatomy. Winslow, whose name is misspelled by Maupertuis, Jacques-Bénigne (1669–1760) was a Dane, converted from Calvinism to Catholicism by Bossuet. His main interest was muscular action.—A.

[26] *Mémoires de l'Académie Royale des Sciences* **1724, 1733, 1734, 1738,** and **1740.** [The discussion in question centered on the dissection of various monsters. Though academicians had introduced reports on monsters earlier, the heat of the debate began in 1733 when Winslow reported on a "girl of twelve, on whose body was attached the lower half of another body, and on the occasion of a two headed fawn dissected by the King's orders." He had been called to the hospital to see whether Extreme Unction should be given to both bodies, but since the

A famous Danish author held another opinion of these monsters. He attributed their creation to the comets. It is a curious but shameful thing for a human mind to find as great a doctor treating comets as abscesses of the sky and prescribing means of warding off their contagion.[27]

---

attached body had neither head, arms, nor chest and since any stimulus given to it was perceived by the subject under investigation, he decided that only one soul inhabited the deformed body and that therefore last rites need not be duplicated. On p. 512 of the same year's reports, he described an eighteen-year-old Italian who had a second head below the cartilage of the third left rib. Both heads had been baptised and given separate names. There was thus in Winslow's mind a religious preoccupation which Maupertuis does not bring out. In 1734 he presented the second half of his report (*Mém. Acad. Sci.* p. 623). In 1738 Lemery reported on the subject, "Quelle est la cause immédiate des monstres?" ("What is the proximate cause of monsters?"), *Mém. Acad. Sci.* **1738,** p. 366 (Pt. 1) and p. 427, (Pt. 2). Winslow came back to the debate in 1740 (*Mém. Acad. Sci.* p. 84) with a report called "Réflexions anatomiques sur les incommodités, infirmités, etc. qui arrivent au corps humain à l'occasion de certaines attitudes et certains habillemens ("Anatomical reflections on the inconveniences, infirmities, and so on which are caused in the human body by certain postures and certain wearing apparel"). Though nothing immediately connected with monsters is mentioned here, the a fortiori argument is indicated to the effect that if sitting hunched over a book, or if high-heeled shoes could cause deformities to the muscles and bones which remained permanent, what might not be expected in the case of the fetus carried by a mother careless of such possibilities? In the same year Lemery published a third memoir on two-headed monsters (pp. 153 and 299) and a fourth, again in two parts (pp. 609 and 723). Winslow submitted a rejoinder on p. 811 and Lemery a rejoinder to Winslow's rejoinder on p. 840. As Maupertuis says, the argument became metaphysical, by which he apparently means theological.—A.

[27] Th[omas] Bartholini *de Cometâ, cum Monstrorum in Daniâ natorum historiâ* (Th[omas] Bartholinus's "Concerning the Comet, Medical Deliberation, together with the story of Monsters born in Denmark"). [Bartholinus was born in 1619 in Copenhagen and died in 1680.—A.]

Chapter Fifteen. *Accidents Brought on by the Imagination of Mothers*

It would seem to me that a more difficult phenomenon to explain than that of the monsters, of which we have been speaking, is the type of monstrosities caused by the mothers' imaginations. There are children to whom their mothers have transferred the face that has frightened them or that has been the object of their admiration and desire. There has often been some anxiety concerning the sudden appearance of a Negro, a monkey, or whatever might surprise or frighten a pregnant woman. Desire for a fruit or other food, difficult to satisfy at the time, is also cause for anxiety regarding women in that condition. Countless stories are told of children bearing the stamp of such accidents.

It would seem to me that those who have been concerned with such phenomena have confused two totally different varieties of experience. That a woman who has been upset by a violent passion, or one finding herself in great peril or terrified by a hideous animal, should give birth to a deformed child seems understandable. Certainly relations between the mother and fetus are close enough for a violent agitation of mind or blood to be transmitted from one to the other. This could induce malformations due to physiological irregularities which the mother's organs might stand, but which would be fatal to the fetus's more delicate parts. Every day we are aware of such involuntary reactions whose sources are much more remote than the mother is from the offspring she carries. When a man walking ahead of me stumbles, my body immediately espouses the attitude that this man should adopt to keep from falling. We can hardly witness the suffering of others without feeling a part of the pain. Often our reactions are more acute than those felt by individuals under fire and sword. This is one of Nature's means of binding men to one another. She induces sympathy in them only when feeling similar pains. Pleasure and suffering are the world's two masters. Without the first, few would bother to continue the species of man, and if it were not for fear of the latter, many would not care to live.

Thus if the fact so often reported be true, that a woman gave birth to a child whose limbs were broken exactly as she had seen a criminal's limbs being broken, it should not be too surprising. The same can be said of other such examples.

But these occurrences should not be confused with those of which we are told where the mother's imagination gave the fetus a face that had frightened her or a fruit that was denied her. Fear may cause important disruptions in the soft parts of the fetus, but these bear no resemblance to that which has caused the fear. I should be more apt to believe that fear of a tiger might cause the death of the fetus or an important deformity than that the child be born with stripes and claws, unless this were entirely a coincidence having nothing to do with the fear of the tiger. Also the child born a rake is much less of a prodigy than the one who might be born with the imprint of a cherry which his mother had wanted to eat, for the feeling a woman experiences through desire or the sight of a fruit in no way resembles the object that aroused the feeling.

However, frequently we encounter faces supposedly bearing the imprint of the mother's desires. Sometimes it is a cherry, sometimes a grape, at other times a fish. I have seen a great many, but I must admit that I have never seen any that cannot be easily explained as some growth or accidental blemish. Once I even saw a mouse on a young woman's neck. Her mother had been terrified by this animal but its image was nothing more than a dark hairy spot such as is sometimes seen on people's cheeks and which remain nameless. Another young lady had on her arm a fish that her mother had wished to eat, but it was only a gray spot.

The reports made by mothers and the memory they have of such and such fears or desires need cause no embarrassment to investigators. Women remember these desires or fears only after they have given birth to children bearing such marks, and the mothers' memory then furnish them with whatever they seek. It is true that in the course of nine months it would be difficult for a woman not to have been afraid of an animal nor have wished to eat a fruit.

Chapter Sixteen. *Difficulties Encountered in*
Ovism and the Theory of Spermatic Animalcules

It is high time to come back to the question of generation. All that we have had to say, far from clarifying the
question, has probably added to doubts. Marvelous facts
of all kinds have been discovered, theories have increased,
and it has become even more difficult to find the answer
sought after in all this great variety.

I know all the faults of these various theories too well
to adopt any and I also find this whole matter too obscure
to dare erect any theory. I have only a few vague ideas
that I propose rather as questions for study than as firm
opinions. I shall neither be surprised nor have cause for
complaint if they are rejected. Furthermore, as it is far
more difficult to discover how a certain result has been
produced than to show that it could not have been produced by such and such means, I shall begin by showing
that neither ovism nor animalculism could reasonably be
accepted.

I should say then that both of these theories are equally
incompatible with Harvey's observation of the formation
of the embryo.

Both of the systems above seem to me to be quite
completely destroyed by the child's resemblance sometimes
to the father and sometimes to the mother, as well as by
hybrid animals born of two different species.

It might not be possible to explain how a child could
resemble his father and mother whatever the means of

their contribution to his generation, but the fact that the
child does resemble both makes us conclude that each one
has an equal share in the child's creation.

We shall not recall Harvey's feeling which reduced the
conception of the child in the womb to a comparison of
the ideas in the brain. What the great man said about
the question can serve only to show how difficult he found
the whole question, or that he tried to arouse people's
more lenient attention towards all ideas proposed, no
matter how strange they appeared.

What seems to have caused him most embarrassment
and thrown him into the comparison above was that he
never found the stag's seed in the doe's uterus. From this
he concluded that the seed did not enter it. But had he
any right to reach this conclusion? The lapse of time
between the coupling of these animals and their dissection
was probably much longer than it would take the semen,
which had entered the uterus, to leak out or be absorbed.

Verheyen's experiment, which proves that the male's
seed does at times enter the uterus, is almost proof that
it always enters, but that it rarely remains in a quantity
sufficient to be actually seen.

Harvey could only have observed a visible quantity of
semen and the fact that he did not find a perceptible
amount does not mean that some drops might not have
been spread over a membrane already moistened by its
own mucus. In spite of the fact that most of the semen
might flow out of the uterus rapidly, or that a very small
amount actually made its way up to mix with the female
fluid, it would be more than enough for the formation of
an embryo.

Consequently I apologize to the modern men of science

for not accepting the theories they have so ingeniously evolved. My reason is that I am not one who believes that scientific progress is made by elaborating systems which are incompatible with certain known phenomena. Some nevertheless continue to erect them and then rest content within their false security.

In spite of the so-called eggs and in spite of the small animalcules observed in seminal fluid, I hardly know whether we should give up the Ancients' ideas on the manner in which generation takes place, which ideas correspond pretty well with Harvey's experiments. When we are tempted to believe that the Ancients held certain opinions because they had not progressed as far as we have, we might be wiser to think that they had actually gone further and that experiments of an earlier date had convinced them of the shortcomings of theories that satisfy us.

It is true that when we say that the embryo is formed by the mixture of the two seminal fluids, we are far from having explained its creation. But the remaining obscurity must not be attributed to our reasoning. He who desires to know a distant object, though he may but see it dimly, is better off than those who do see clearly distant objects that are not the ones sought.

Although I have the deepest respect for Descartes and believe, as he does, that the fetus is formed from the mixture of the two seminal fluids, I cannot believe that anyone is satisfied with the explanation which he gives. It seems incredible that the creation of an animal should originate from the mixture of two fluids through an intelligible mechanism. However hidden the key to this wonder may be, I shall believe in it.

Chapter Seventeen. *Hypotheses on the Formation of the Fetus*

In this obscurity in which we find ourselves concerning the fetus's creation from the mixture of two fluids, we come upon certain facts that are perhaps a better analogy than what takes place in the brain. When silver, spirits of niter, mercury, and water are mixed together, the various particles of these substances arrange themselves in a pattern so similar to that of a tree, that the result is called the *Arbor Dianae* [arborescent silver]. Since the discovery of this admirable "vegetation," many others have been found. One of them, of which iron is the basic metal, imitates a tree so completely that not only are a trunk, branches, roots, to be seen, but leaves and fruit as well.[28] What a miracle it would seem if such vegetation were created out of sight! Familiarity lessens the miraculous character of most of nature's phenomena.[29] When the eyes become accustomed to seeing them, we believe we understand them, but for the Philosopher the mystery remains. His only conclusion can be that there are actual facts of which he does not know the causes and his senses are there to humiliate his mind.

Doubtless many other similar productions will be found

---

[28] *Mémoires de l'Académie Royale des Sciences* **1706**, [p. 529. This is a report by Lemery, *fils,* "Que les Plantes contiennent réellement du fer." The so-called tree is described on p. 534 and it is suggested that it be called the Tree of Mars.—A.]

[29] Quid non in miraculo est, cum primum in notitiam venit? ["What is not miraculous when it first comes to notice?"—A.] Pliny, "Natural History," Book VII, Chap. 1.

if we look for them or possibly when we are not searching. Although these seem less highly organized than the bodies of most animals, might they not depend on the same mechanisms and on similar laws? Could the ordinary laws of motion suffice, or should we call upon new forces for help?

Such forces, however incomprehensible, seem to have penetrated into the *Académie des Sciences,* where so many opinions are examined before being accepted. One of the most famous members of this academy, whose loss will be long regretted by our sciences, looked deeply into nature's secrets and saw the faultiness of reducing her operations to the common laws of motion.[30] He then had recourse to forces which he felt would be more apt to be received favorably under the name of *relations.* These relations mean that *whenever two substances have a tendency to join each other, they become united, and if a third substance arises that seems to have a stronger attraction for one than the other, it unites with that one, causing the other to let go.*[31]

I cannot fail to call attention to the fact that these forces and relations are nothing but what other bolder Philosophers call *Attraction.* This ancient term, brought back in our time, at first worried the Physicists who believed it possible to explain all natural phenomena without its use. The Astronomers were the first to feel the need of a new

[30] M. Geoffroy. [Maupertuis is referring to Etienne François Geoffroy, 1672–1731, who was primarily a chemist, particularly interested in the "affinities" of various substances. He published a table of such, known as the *tables des rapports.* The relations mentioned in the body of the text are these *rapports.*—A.]

[31] *Mémoires de l'Académie des Sciences* **1718.** [The law is given on p. 257, as quoted by Maupertuis.—A.]

principle to explain the movements of the celestial bodies
and thought they had discovered it in these very movements. Since then chemistry has felt the same necessity of
adopting this concept, and the most famous Chemists
admit Attraction and extend its function farther than had
been done by the Astronomers.

Why should not a cohesive force, if it exists in Nature,
have a role in the formation of animal bodies? If there
are, in each of the seminal seeds, particles predetermined
to form the heart, the head, the entrails, the arms and the
legs, if these particular particles had a special attraction
for those which are to be their immediate neighbors in
the animal body, this would lead to the formation of the
fetus. Even though the fetus were a thousand times more
complex, if the process above were exact, it would still be
formed.

We should not believe that in both male and female
seed there are just the number of parts necessary to form
one fetus, or whatever number of offspring the female is
supposed to produce. Both sexes undoubtedly provide a
much greater quantity than is necessary. When two parts
that should touch each other become united, a third which
could have served the same function no longer finds a
place, it then becomes useless. With these repeated operations the child is formed from particles coming both from
the father and the mother and he frequently shows visible
proof of the dual participation.

If each particle is united with those meant to be its
neighbors, and to no others, the child is born perfect. If,
on the contrary, some parts find themselves too far or of
unsuitable shapes or too weak for close union with the
precise particles, then a *monster by default* is born. But

if some superfluous parts still find an available place for union in spite of the fact that the acceptable number is already complete, then there is a *monster by excess.*

A comment on this last type of monster is so favorable to our theory that it could be used as proof. This is the fact that the superfluous parts are always found in the same area as the normal parts. If a monster has two heads, they are both set on the same neck or on a union of two vertebrae. If there are two bodies, they are joined in the same manner. There are many examples of men born with extra fingers, but these are always found attached either to hands or feet.[32] If it were accepted that these freaks are the result of the union of two eggs or of two embryos, how could this union occur in such a way as to insure that the remaining parts of the injured one would become linked to the normal parts of the embryo which had suffered no injury? I have seen an even more decisive example of this in the skeleton of a giant. The only apparent deformity was an extra vertebra placed in line with the other vertebrae forming the spine.[33] How could

[32] Yet Maupertuis also refers to *mémoires* reported in the Academy of Sciences in which, e.g., the lower part of a body was attached to a girl's trunk and a boy had a second head below the cartilage of his third left rib. See *Mémoires de l'Académie Royale des Sciences* **1733**, Winslow's *"Remarques sur les monstres, etc.,"* Pt. 1, pp. 508 ff. and **1734**, pp. 623 ff.—A.

[33] This strange skeleton is in the Anatomical Hall of the Royal Academy of Sciences and Letters. Here is the description of it, sent to me by M. Buddaeus, Professor of Anatomy. "In accordance with your orders which I received yesterday, I have the honor to very humbly inform you that there is indeed in our Amphitheatre a skeleton which has one extra vertebra. It is seven feet tall, and His Majesty the late King has sent it here to be cared for because of its rarity. I have carefully examined it and my conclusion is that the supernumerary vertebra must be classified as one of the lumbar region. The vertebrae of the neck have their peculiar marks. But this one surely is not one of them, still less one from the back, since the ribs are characteristic of

one believe that this vertebra could be the remains of an embryo?

If we insisted that monsters should be born from originally monstrous seed, is our difficulty any the less? Why should monstrous seed observe this strict order in the organization of their parts? Why should ears never be found on feet nor fingers on the head?

As to human monsters having either cats' or dogs' or horses' heads, I shall wait until I have seen one before trying to give an explanation of their production. I have examined several freaks said to be of this type, but all that could be found was some deformity in features. Never have I found an individual showing signs of parts belonging indubitably to a species other than its own. And if I should be shown a minotaur or a centaur, I would be more apt to believe in a crime than in a prodigy.

It seems that the idea we have proposed on the formation of the fetus satisfies more completely than any other the phenomena of generation based on the resemblance of the child to the father and the mother; or of the hybrid animals born of two different species; of both types of monsters, and finally as being the only idea able to stand up to Harvey's observations.

---

them. The first lumbar vertebra has its own natural conformity in relation to its union with the twelfth dorsal, and the last lumbar vertebra has its usual shape which fits it to the *os sacrum*. Therefore the supernumerary one must have its place between the other lumbar vertebrae, that is, between the first and the last lumbar.

Chapter Eighteen. *Hypotheses on the Function of Spermatic Animalcules*

What will become of the small animals discovered in the male semen with the use of a microscope? What function has nature intended for them? We shall not deny their existence, as some Anatomists have done, for it would show poor usage of a microscope not to have seen them. But we can well be ignorant of their use. Could they be of some use in the production of the animal without actually being the animal itself? Perhaps their only function is to insure movement in the prolific liquids and so bring together distant parts and facilitate their union with their mates.

I have looked in vain with an excellent microscope for similar animalcules in the fluid emitted by the female. Still I would not insist that they were not there. Beyond the fluid that I think of as prolific in women, but which is perhaps of a minor quantity and may remain in the uterus, there are others about which mistakes can be made. Numberless circumstances can easily make such observations dubious. But if there were animalcules in woman's seminal fluid, they would serve the same purpose as those of the male. And if there are none, man's are apparently sufficient to stir and mix the two fluids.

Do not be surprised by the use we attribute to the spermatic animals, as Nature, apart from her major agents, often makes use of minor ministers. In the Archipelago Islands a species of gnats is raised with the greatest care in order that they may fertilize figs.[34]

---

[34] See the Voyage in the Levant of Tournefort. [Joseph Pitton de Tournefort (1656–1708), a botanist, one of whose most famous books was the "Institutiones rei herbariae," Paris, 1700. He was commissioned by the king to make a collection of the flora of the Middle East and Greece and spent three years there. The result, published in the book to which Maupertuis refers, is a series of letters, "Relation d'un Voyage du Levant," Lyon, 1717.—A.]

Part Two

Varieties in the Species of Man

Chapter One. *Distribution of the Different Races of Man, According to the Earth's Different Areas*

Had the first white men who saw black men, encountered them in forests, they might not have called them men. But in turn, those found in large cities, governed by wise queens who caused the arts and sciences to flourish at a time when all other peoples were still barbarians, might not have wished to accept the whites as brother.[35]

From the Tropic of Cancer to the Tropic of Capricorn Africa has only black inhabitants. They are distinguished by their color as well as their facial features. The nose is broad and flat, the lips are thick, and there is wool instead of hair, all of which seems to indicate a new species of man.[36]

Moving from the Equator towards the Antarctic Pole the color becomes lighter, but the ugly features remain and on the southernmost point of Africa an unattractive race, the Hottentots, is found.

Traveling up towards the Orient, we shall find peoples whose features become softer and more regular, but their color is as dark as the African.

[35] Diodorus Siculus, Book III, ii.
[36] Manilius, Book IV, lines 723–724.
> Aethiopes maculant orbem, tenebrisque figurant,
> Per fuscas hominum gentes.

["The Ethiopians spot the world and adorn it with shadowy forms by dusky tribes of man." Housman in his edition of Manilius reads in line 724 "perfusas hominum gentes," which could be translated "they represent races of men wrapped in shadows."—A.]

After these come a great people of swarthy complexion, distinct from other peoples by their long, narrow eyes set on the oblique.

Should we go into the vast part of the world that seems separated from Europe, Africa, and Asia, we would find, as might be expected, many new types. There are no whites. That land, peopled by reddish and swarthy nations of countless shades, ends towards the Antarctic Pole with a cape and islands inhabited by giants, so we are told. If we are to believe the stories of several voyagers, there is a race of men at this extreme end of America whose height is practically twice ours.

Before leaving our continent, we might have spoken of another kind of man quite different from these. The inhabitants of the northernmost part of Europe are the smallest that are known. The Lapps in the North, the Patagonians in the South, would seem to be the extreme types of the human species.

I never would finish if I spoke of the inhabitants in the islands of the Indian Sea and in the vast ocean which fills the space between Asia and America. Each people, each nation, has its own characteristics and its own tongue.[37]

If we should travel over all these islands, we should perhaps find some inhabitants far more puzzling to us than the blacks and to whom it would be difficult either to refuse or to assign the name of man. Do the inhabitants of the Borneo forests, spoken of by travelers, and who are

[37] Manilius, Book IV, lines 731–732.
  Adde sonos totidem vocum, totidem insere linguas,
  Et mores pro sorte pares, ritusque locorum.
["Think too of the sounds of so many words, of so many languages, and of customs determined by fortune, and of local religions."—A.]

so similar to men, think less well for having tails like monkeys? Should that classification which we have not made dependent on the color white or black be made according to the number of vertebrae?

On the Isthmus that separates the northern ocean from the Pacific, we are told,[38] men, whiter than any known to us, are found. Their hair might be mistaken for the whitest of wools. Their blue eyes, too feeble to stand daylight, open only in the darkness of night. They are in the human species what bats and owls are in the realm of birds. When the light of day has disappeared and has left nature in mourning and silence; when all other inhabitants of the earth, exhausted from labor or tired of pleasure, give in to sleep, the Darien awakens, praises his gods, rejoices over the absence of an insufferable light, and comes to fill the void of nature. He listens to the owl's cries with as much pleasure as our shepherds hear the lark's song when with dawn's first light, out of the hawk's sight, she seems to soar into the clouds to seek daylight that has not yet come to earth. She indicates through her wings' beat the cadence of her song, and as she rises, is lost in the air. She no longer is seen but still heard and the sounds no longer distinct inspire tenderness and reverie. That moment unites the peace of night with the pleasures of day. The sun appears, bringing to earth movement and life. With it come the hours and man's various labors. The Dariens have not waited for this moment to retire, but perhaps might we find still a few at

[38] Voyage of Wafer, description of the Isthmus of America. [Lionel Wafer (1660?–1705?) wrote a description of the Isthmus of Panama, now available in English under the title "A New Voyage and Description of the Isthmus of America" (G. P. Winship, ed.). Cleveland, 1903.—A.]

table who after having filled their stomachs with stew exhaust their minds with draughts and sword-play. But the only sensible man who is awake is he who awaits noon for a tryst. It is the perfect time, favored by the height of daylight, to choose in order to outdo a mother's vigilance and meet his timid lover.

The most remarkable phenomenon and the most constant law concerning color in the earth's inhabitants is that the wide band round the globe from the Orient to the Occident, called the Torrid Zone, is inhabited only by black or darkly colored people. In spite of the indentations caused by the seas, whether we follow this zone across Africa, Asia, and America, whether over islands or continents, we find only black nations, for the nocturnal men, just mentioned, and a few whites born there hardly deserve our making an exception.

Leaving the Equator the color of the people becomes lighter in shade. It remains dark beyond the Tropic and becomes really white only when the temperate zone is reached. At the extreme edges of that zone the whitest people are to be found. The Danish woman with her blond hair and white skin dazzles the surprised traveler. He can hardly believe that the creature before him and the African woman he has just seen can both be women.

Farther still towards the north, up to the frozen zone, in the land that the sun hardly deigns to light in winter and where the earth is harder than stone and sustains none of the produce of other lands, are found lily and rose complexions.

Rich countries of the South, land of Peru and Potosi, though you may produce gold in your mines, I shall not be the one to dig it out. Golconda, though you may filter the precious substance from which diamonds and rubies are made, they will not make your women beautiful and are useless to ours. They will serve only to tally the weight and wealth of a stupid monarch,[39] each year, who while he stands on those ridiculous scales loses both his realm and his liberty.

In those extreme lands where all are white or all are black, is there not too complete a uniformity? Would not a mixture produce new beauty? It is on the banks of the Seine that this happy variety is found. On a fine day, in the Gardens of the Louvre, you can see the marvels that the whole earth can produce.

A brunette with black eyes glistens with all the fire of southern beauty, while blue eyes soften the features of another. These eyes carry with them everywhere the charm of the blond. Brown hair seems to be the national color. The French woman neither has the vivacity of those burnt by the sun nor the languor of those who never feel its warmth, but she possesses all that is pleasing. What radiance is hers! She would seem to be fashioned of alabaster, gold, and azure! I love in her even Nature's mistakes, such as making her hair too harsh in color. She then made up for it by a new shade of white which is far from being a fault and should not be tampered with by the use of powder. Beauties of this type, do let the roses of your complexion spread and carry life right into your hair. . . . I have seen green eyes among these beauties and I recognized them from afar, for they resembled neither the southerners nor the northerners.

[39] The Great Mogul has himself weighed annually and the weight put on the scales is diamonds and rubies. He has just been dethroned by Kuli Khan and reduced to being a vassal of the kings of Persia.

In those delightful Gardens the number of beauties is far greater than that of the flowers and to our eyes there is always one more beautiful than the others. Pick these flowers, but do not gather them together. Flit about, lovers, look them all over, but always return to one, if you wish to savor the pleasures of your heart.

Chapter Two. *An Explanation of the Phenomenon of Color Difference in Ovism and Animalculism*

Have all these different peoples we have just enumerated, with such a diversity of men, come from one mother? We cannot doubt it.

What remains to be explained is how one individual can have given birth to so many different races. I shall attempt some conjectures.

If men all began by being formed from one egg inside another, there must have been in the first mother eggs of different colors. These must have contained an innumerable series of the same kind of eggs, to hatch only in their proper order of development, after a number of generations and at the time Providence had intended for the origin of the peoples so contained. It might not be impossible that some day when the series of white eggs giving birth to the peoples of our region has come to an end, all European nations will change color. Just as it might not be impossible that when the black eggs have given out, Ethiopia would then have only white inhabitants. This is what happens in a deep quarry when the vein of white marble has come to an end and only stones of various colors are to be found, one after another. So new races of men may appear on earth while ancient ones disappear.

Were we to accept the system of animalcules and say that all men had been originally contained inside the animals swimming in the first man's semen, we would have to repeat about animalcules what we have just said about eggs. So the worm, father of all Negroes, contained from worm to worm all the inhabitants of Ethiopia; and the same would be true of the Darien worm, the Hottentot worm, and the Patagonian, with all their descendants already formed and destined one day to people the parts of the globe inhabited by their races.

Chapter Three. *Production of New Species*

The theories above of eggs and worms may lend themselves too easily to the explanation of the origin of blacks and whites. They even try to explain how different species have come from the same individuals, but we saw in the preceding analysis what difficulties arise.

The varieties in the human species are not reduced to white or black but there are a thousand others. Those that strike us easily are probably not more difficult for Nature to create than others barely noticeable. If it were possible to understand the principle from decisive experiments, it might not seem stranger for a white child to be born from black parents than it would be for a blue-eyed child to come from a line of black-eyed ancestors.

Children usually resemble their parents and the variations among them at birth are often the results of various resemblances. Could we follow these variations back, we might find their origin in a common but unknown ancestor. They are kept alive by generations that have these traits and fade out with generations which do not have them. But what is even more surprising is to find such variations reappearing after having disappeared. We find a child who resembles neither his father nor his mother but has the features of his grandfather. Such facts, though amazing, are too frequent to be considered as doubtful.

Nature holds the source of all these varieties, but chance or art sets them going. So that people whose work is to satisfy the tastes of curiosity seekers become practically creators of new species. We find new breeds of dogs, pigeons, canaries appearing on the market, though they did not exist in nature. At first they were individual freaks, but art and repeated generations turned them into new species. The famed Lyonnés[40] creates each year a new variety and destroys the ones no longer in style. He corrects the shapes and varies the colors to the point of inventing species, such as the Harlequin Dane and the *Mopse* [Pug dog].

Why is this art restricted to animals? Why don't the bored Sultans in their seraglios, filled with women of all known races, have them bear new species? Were I reduced, as they are, to the only pleasure that form and features can give, I would soon have recourse to greater varieties. But, however beautiful the women born for them might be, they would know only the smallest share of love's pleasures as long as they remained ignorant of the pleasures of the mind and the heart.

Although we do not find among ourselves the creation of such new types of beauty, only too often do we see human beings who are of the same category for men of science, namely, the cross-eyed, the lame, the gouty, and the tubercular. Unfortunately, in order to fix their strain there is no need of a long series of generations. But wise Nature, because of the disgust she has inspired for these defects, has not desired that they be continued. Conse-

---

[40] Pierre Lyonnet, as the name is spelled in the various reference books, was born in Maestricht in 1707 and died in 1789. He was an artist and engraver as well as a naturalist, illustrating Lesser's "Théologie des insectes" (French translation in 1742). He also made the drawings for Trembley's "Mémoire pour servir à l'histoire d'un nouveau genre de polypes d'eau douce" ("Preliminary essay towards the natural history of a new genus"—or perhaps species—"of freshwater polyp").—A.

quently beauty is more apt to be hereditary. The slim waist and the leg that we admire are the achievements of many generations which have applied themselves to form them.

A Northern king was able to elevate and beautify his nation. His taste for men of height and fine faces was excessive and he induced them to come to his kingdom by various means. Fortune came to men whom Nature had made tall. Today we now see a singular example of the power of kings. This nation is distinguished for its tall men and regular features. So it is with a forest whose trees dominate all the neighboring woods, if the attentive eye of the master forester takes care to cultivate only trees that are straight and well chosen. The oak and the elm, adorned with the greenest of leaves, lift their branches to the sky where only the eagle can reach their crest. This king's successor today adorns the forest with laurel, myrtle, and flowers.

The Chinese once believed that the greatest beauty for women was to have feet so small that they could not stand on them. This nation, deeply attached to following the opinions and taste of its ancestors, finally reached the point of having women with ridiculous feet. I have seen Chinese women's mules into which our women could barely put a toe. This type of beauty is not new. Pliny, quoting Eudoxus, speaks of a people in India whose women have such small feet that they were called ostriches' feet.[41] It is true that he adds that men's feet measured a cubit and it might be that the smallness of the

[41] Pliny, "Natural History," Book VII, Chap. ii [Ed. Sillig, 1852, Vol. II, p. 9. Properly speaking, *struthopodes* should be translated "sparrow-footed" but Maupertuis was probably recalling the "great sparrows" of Xenophon.—A.]

women's feet led to exaggerating the size of the men's. Was not this nation, China, little known at the time? As a matter of fact the small size of Chinese women's feet cannot be attributed to nature, for during early childhood their feet are bound tightly to keep them from growing. In spite of this it would seem that Chinese women are born with smaller feet than women of other nations. This is a strange statement to make and it deserves attention from travelers.

Fatal beauty, the desire to please—what disorders do you not cause in the world! Not only do you torment our hearts, but you change nature's order. When a young French woman mocks the Chinese, she is not blaming her for thinking that she will be more attractive by sacrificing a graceful walk to the smallness of her feet. She knows at heart that this is not too high a price to pay for being charming, even if it means torture and pain. She herself since childhood has her body encased in a contraption of whalebone, or firmly held by an iron cross, both of which are more uncomfortable than all the bands tightened round the feet of the Chinese. Her head at night, bristling with curlers instead of being wrapped in the softness of her hair, can rest only on sharp points. In spite of this she sleeps peacefully, resting on her charms.

Chapter Four. *White Negroes*

Willingly would I forget the phenomenon that I shall attempt to explain and attend to Iris's awakening. But I must relate the history of a little freak.

This is a child of four or five whose features are entirely negroid and whose very white and pale skin only enhances his ugliness.[42] His head is covered by white wool with a reddish tinge. His eyes are light blue and seem hurt by bright daylight. His hands, large and misshapen, resemble more an animal's paws than the hands of a man. He is the offspring, we are told, of African parents, both black.

The *Académie des Sciences* of Paris mentions a similar monster born in Surinam of African parentage.[43] His mother was black and insisted that it was also true of his father. The Academy's historian seems to doubt the latter and thinks the father was a white Negro. This I do not believe to be necessary. It would suffice for the child to have had a white Negro among his ancestors or he might even be the first one of his race.

In a collection full of curiosities owned by the Countess of V., there is the portrait of a white Negro. Though the subject represented is actually in Spain and much older than the one in Paris, I was told by Lord M. that he had seen him. Again we note the same complexion, the same eyes, and the same cast of features.

[42] He was brought to Paris in 1744.
[43] *Histoire de l'Académie des Sciences,* 1734.

I have been told positively that in the Senegal there are whole families of this type and that even in black families there are fairly frequent examples of the birth of white Negroes.

America and Africa are not the only parts of the world where such freaks are found. Asia also has produced them. Monsieur du Mas, a man of great distinction and merit who occupied a high post in the East Indies and whose love of truth is well known, saw white Negroes amidst blacks, whose whiteness was inherited from father to son. He willingly satisfied my curiosity and related that the whiteness was like a skin disease, an accident that was transmissible and lasted through several generations.[44]

I was delighted to find the ideas of such a cultivated man coinciding with mine concerning that type of monster. Whether the whiteness is taken for a sickness or for whatever accident one chooses, it can only be of an hereditary variety which becomes established or disappears with successive generations.

Such variations in color are more frequent in animals than in man. Blackness is just as inherent in crows and blackbirds as it is in Negroes, but I have often seen white crows and white blackbirds. Such varieties would undoubtedly become breeds if they were cultivated. I have been in countries where all the hens are white. The whiteness of their skin, usually linked with the whiteness of their feathers, has given priority to these fowl and from generation to generation their stability has been achieved.

As a matter of fact it is most likely that the difference

---

[44] Maupertuis in a footnote corrects the word "skin" by substituting the *membrane réticulaire,* which is presumably the Malpighian layer. A.

between whiteness and blackness, which is so apparent to our eyes, is but a slight thing in nature. A mild alteration to the blackest horse's skin causes the growth of white hairs without any intermediary colors.

Should we feel the need of investigating the realm of plants in order to confirm my statement, we would be told by gardeners that all the variegated colors we find in shrubs and flowers, highly prized in our gardens, are due to selections which have become hereditary but which will revert if neglected.[45]

---

[45] Vidi lecta diu, et multo spectata labore,

Degenerare tamen; ni vis humana quot annis

Maxima quaeque manu legeret.—Virgil, *Georgics,* I, 197–199. ["I have seen seeds, chosen and inspected long and with much care, nevertheless degenerate, even if the force of man year by year had chosen the greatest by hand." (Thus all things by the force of fate have turned to the worse.)—A.]

Chapter Five. *Attempt at an Explanation of the Preceding Phenomena*

In order to explain all the phenomena above: the accidental production of varieties, the succession of such varieties from one generation to the next, and finally the establishment of the destruction of these breeds, this, I believe, is what faces us. If what I am about to say is revolting to you, just consider it as an effort toward a satisfactory explanation. I do not expect it to be complete, for the phenomena are most complex. At least much shall be accomplished if I have been able to link these phenomena to others on which they are dependent.

We should take for granted facts that experience forces upon us:

(1) That seminal fluid from members of each species of animal contains a multitude of parts suitable to the formation of animals of the same species;

(2) That in the seminal fluid of each individual the parts suitable for the formation of features similar to those of that individual are normally in greater number and have a stronger affinity for one another. There are also many others which may form different features;

(3) As to the matter of the seminal fluid of each animal from which parts resembling it are to be formed, it would be an audacious guess, but might not be unlikely, to suggest that each part furnishes its germs. Experiments might throw light on this point. If it were tried for a long

time to mutilate some animals of the same breed, generation after generation, perhaps we might find the amputated parts diminishing little by little. Finally, one might see them disappear.[46]

The guesses above seem necessary and, once we admit them, it may seem possible to explain the many phenomena we have explored.

Parts similar to those of the father and mother, being the most numerous as well as having the greatest affinity, will be the ones to unite most easily and then will form animals like the ones from which they came.

Chance or a shortage of family traits will at times cause other combinations, and then we may see a white child born of black parents, or even a black child from white parents, though this is a much rarer phenomenon than the former.

I am speaking here only of these strange occurrences when a child born of parents of the same race has traits which he does not inherit from them, for we know that when the races are mixed, the child inherits from both.

The unusual unions of parts which are not the parts similar to those of the parents are really freaks to the bold who seek an explanation of Nature's wonders. For the wise man, satisfied with the spectacle, they are beauties.

To begin with, these latter productions are accidental, for the parts whose origin is ancestral are the more abundant in the seeds. Therefore after a few generations, or even in the next generation, the original species will regain its strength and the child, instead of resembling its father or

[46] It may perhaps be superfluous to recall the experiment of Weismann here, since it is well known. But at least it is worth pointing out that it was anticipated by Maupertuis.—A.

mother, will resemble some distant ancestor.[47] In order to create species from races that become established, it is really necessary to have the same types unite for several generations. The parts suitable to recreate the original trait, since they are less numerous in each generation, are either lost or remain in so small a quantity that a new chance event would be needed to reproduce the original species. However, though I imagine the basic stock of all these varieties is to be found in the seminal fluids themselves, I do not exclude the possible influence of climate and food. It would seem that the heat of the Torrid Zone is more favorable to the particles that compose black skin than to those that make up white skin. And I simply do not know how far this kind of influence of climate and food may go after many centuries.

It would indeed be something to occupy the attention of Philosophers if they would try to discover whether certain unnatural characters induced in animals for many generations were transmitted to their descendants. Whether tails or ears cut off from generation to generation did diminish in size or even finally disappear would be of importance.

One thing is certain, and that is that all variations which may characterize new breeds of animals and plants tend to degenerate. They are the sports of Nature, only preserved through art or discipline, for her original creations always tend to return.

---

[47] This happens daily in families. A child who resembles neither his father nor his mother will resemble a grandparent.

Chapter Six. *That It Is Rarer to Have Black Children Born of White Parents, Than White Children of Black Parents. That the Original Parents of the Human Race Were White. The Difficulty of the Origin of the Black Is Raised.*

From these sudden births of white children among black peoples it might be concluded that white was man's original color and that blackness was only a variation that had become hereditary after many centuries. But whiteness was not completely eradicated in the black race and tends to reappear. We do not find the opposite phenomenon, of black children born of white ancestors.

I know that it has been said that this prodigy has been known to occur in France but there is so little sufficient proof that it cannot reasonably be accepted. Man's taste for the extraordinary must always make us suspicious of the prodigious when it has not been proved. A child is born with a deformity and the women who are in attendance immediately turn him into a frightful monster. If his skin is darker than is usual, he becomes a Negro. But everyone who has seen Negro children born knows that they are not black at birth and that for the early days of their life it would be difficult to tell them from other children. Hence if a Negro child were born to a white family, it would remain uncertain that he was one for some time. Nor would anyone think of hiding the fact. It would be impossible not to admit his existence for the early months and later hide his disappearance, particularly if his parents were well known. And the Negro born among the common people, once he had attained his full color, would be a prodigy and an asset because of general curiosity. Most people anyway would love their son, black or white.

However, if these prodigies were fairly frequent, the numerical probability is that they would more likely arise among the common people rather than among the upper class, and considering the mathematical relation of the two classes, for each black child born to a great nobleman, there would have to be a thousand among the masses. How could these facts be ignored? Could they be doubted?

If there are white children born among the blacks and if this phenomenon is not exceedingly rare among the numerous people of Africa and America, how much more frequent should these births of blacks be among the innumerable people of Europe, if nature allowed such hazards with equal ease. Furthermore, if we become aware of these phenomena when they arise in far distant countries, why should we be ignorant of similar ones if they occurred in our midst?

It would then seem to me an established fact that if black children are born to white parents, these births are far more rare than births of white children to black parents. This might suffice to lead us to think that white was the original color of man, and that black became an hereditary color in the great racial families of the Torrid Zone simply through some accident. But even there, the primitive color has not been so completely eliminated that it does not reappear at times.

If we admit a system concerning generation that is at least as likely as all the others conceived so far, the difficulty over the origin of the blacks, so often repeated, has at least been solved. It has even been used by some to fight history according to Genesis, which would teach us that all the peoples of the earth came from one father and one mother.

Chapter Seven. *Why Should the Blacks Be Found Only in the Torrid Zone and Dwarfs and Giants Near the Poles?*

We shall find, and even among us, other monsters which undoubtedly come from fortuitous combinations of particles in the seed or the effect of too great or too weak an attraction between these particles. Some result in men of excessive height and others of extremely small size which make them seem like freaks. They might become races if they were multiplied systematically.

If we are to believe what travelers from the territories of the Strait of Magellan and the northern extremities of the earth have said, the Giants and Dwarfs settled there either because the climate suited them or, more probably, because they were driven to these far regions by other peoples who feared these colossuses and scorned the Pygmies.

Whether Giants, Dwarfs, or Blacks were born among other men, either fear or pride aroused antagonism towards them on the part of the greater portion of the human race. The strongest and most numerous races then relegated these abnormal people to the least habitable zones. The Dwarfs retired towards the North Pole and the Giants went to live near the Strait of Magellan, while the Blacks settled in the Torrid Zone.

Conclusion. *Doubts and Questions*

I have no hope that this sketchy account of theories proposed by us as an explanation of the formation of animals will please everyone. I am not entirely satisfied with it myself, and I grant it only the degree of approval which it deserves. All I have done is put forth doubts and conjectures. Before we can discover anything concerning such an obscure subject, here are a few questions that will first have to be answered and which may never be.

I

Does not that instinct, found in animals causing them to seek what suits them and flee from what harms them, also exist in the animal's smallest particles? Is not this instinct, though dispersed among the particles of the seeds and weaker in each than it is in the whole animal, sufficient to effect the unions necessary between these particles? This would seem likely as we note that in completely formed animals that instinct causes their limbs to move. Although it be said that such movements are executed by an intelligible mechanism or that they can be explained by the tensing and relaxing of the muscles, caused either by a flow or an absence of blood and spirits, it would still be necessary to come back to the movement of the spirits and the blood which are directed by the will. And if the will is not the real cause of these movements, but simply an occasional cause, might we not think that instinct could also be a cause of motion and union in the small particles of matter? And because of some pre-established harmony, these movements would always be in accord with the will.

II

Is this instinct, like the guiding spirit of a Republic, spread throughout all parts of the body? Or, as in a Monarchy, is it a function of one indivisible part?

If this is the case, would not this particular part properly constitute the essence of the animal while all others would be only envelopes or kinds of outer coverings?

III

At death would not this essential part survive? Separated from all others, might it not preserve its unalterable essence, always ready to produce an animal, or better yet, to reappear in a new body? After having disappeared in the air or in water, hidden within the leaves of plants or in the flesh of animals, could it have been saved for the seed of the animal it was to reproduce?

IV

Could this part ever reproduce only one animal of the same species? Or could it reproduce all possible varieties through the mere diversity of the combination of the union of parts?[48]

---

[40] Non omnis moriar; multaque pars mei
     Vitabit Libitinam. Horace, *Carmina*, Book III, xxx, 6.
["I shall not die entirely, and a great part of me shall escape Death."
—A.]